THE ENGLISH WORKBOOK

DEVELOPING LITERACY

Writing forms

Speaking

Grammar

Spelling

Narrative

Procedure

Listening

Report

Reading

Exposition

Proofreading

Recount

Vocabulary

Evaluation

Editing

Diane Henderson   Rosemary Morris   Jenepher Snell

Prim-Ed
Publishing

The English workbook *(Book F)*

Published by Prim-Ed Publishing 2013
Reprinted 2015

Copyright© Diane Henderson, Rosemary Morris, Jenepher Snell 2007

ISBN 978-1-84654-644-0
PR–6281

Titles available in this series:
The English workbook *(Book A)*
The English workbook *(Book B)*
The English workbook *(Book C)*
The English workbook *(Book D)*
The English workbook *(Book E)*
The English workbook *(Book F)*
The English workbook *(Book G)*

Introduction

This workbook is all about procedures, recounts, expositions, narratives and reports. These are called writing formats. There are two units of work based on each format.

Completing the exercises in your workbook will help you to understand the five different formats and to learn how to plan and write them yourself.

You will be:

- discussing and working out the structure of each format
- checking that you understand the text by doing some comprehension exercises
- working to improve your vocabulary, spelling, punctuation and grammar
- practising different writing skills
- learning how to check your writing by editing and proofreading
- checking how much you have learned by doing a test at the end of each unit.

Remember: *Good writers need to think about, plan and review their writing; it doesn't just happen.*

Contents

Contents

Contents

The English workbook

Hamburgers

This procedure explains **how to do something**.
The main purpose of a procedure is to **direct**, **inform** or **explain**.

Read the **procedure**.

Hamburgers

Ingredients:

10 hamburger buns
500 g minced beef
1 egg
1 carrot (grated)
1 large potato (grated)
1 cup breadcrumbs
2 tablespoons tomato sauce
2 tablespoons soy sauce
Salad (tomatoes, shredded lettuce, beetroot, cucumber)
Extra tomato sauce

Method

1. Mix all ingredients in a bowl.
2. Make 10 balls of equal size.
3. Flatten balls into a round shape.
4. Cook burgers in a greased pan for about 5 minutes, then turn and cook for 4-5 minutes on medium heat.
5. Allow burgers to drain on absorbent paper.
6. Cut buns in half.
7. Add burgers, salad and tomato sauce.

Enjoy!

Partner activity

1. Discuss reasons why recipes are written down. Record your ideas.

   Recipes are written down because

   - _____
   - _____
   - _____
   - _____
   - _____

   There are many well-known chefs or cooks who appear on television, or radio, or who write cook books.

2. Discuss and make a list of well-known cooks. You may need to research to add to your list.

Structure of a procedure

This procedure has:	
A goal:	This is at the beginning and tells us what is to be done.
Requirements:	These are items needed to complete a task. It could be ingredients for a recipe, tools for changing a car tyre or maps and a compass for finding directions.
Steps:	This is a list, in order, of what you must do.
Test:	This is the conclusion which confirms the success of the procedure.

Read the recipe for making hamburgers again and answer the following questions about the structure of a procedure.

Goal

1. What is the purpose of this procedure? _____

_____

_____

Requirements

2. What do you need to complete this task? _____

_____

_____

_____

Steps

3. The order of the steps in a procedure can be very important. Colour the instructions or steps you would follow first.

(a)	Mix ingredients.	OR	Place ingredients in a bowl.
(b)	Make 10 balls of equal size.	OR	Flatten balls to make round shape.
(c)	Drain burgers.	OR	Cook for five minutes.
(d)	Add salad.	OR	Enjoy the hamburgers.

Test

4. How would you know if you have followed the procedure correctly?

_____

_____

WORKING WITH THE TEXT **Reading**

Reading for information

True or false? Colour the correct answer.

1. This recipe will make six hamburgers. ○ true ○ false

2. The egg must be added to the mixture after all the other ingredients. ○ true ○ false

3. The burgers need to be cooked over low heat. ○ true ○ false

4. Both the carrot and the potatoes need to be grated before being added to the mixture. ○ true ○ false

5. The burgers need to be cooked in an oven. ○ true ○ false

Reading for understanding

1. Do you think that this recipe is easy to make? _____
   Explain your answer.

   _____

   _____

   _____

2. Why would you need to place the burgers on absorbent paper before putting them inside the buns?

3. Do you think these hamburgers are healthy food and good for you? _____
   Explain your answer.

   _____

   _____

   _____

4. Do you think both girls and boys should learn to cook? _____
   Give reasons for your answer.

5. In restaurants, most chefs are male. Why do you think this is? _____

   _____

   _____

   _____

Applying your knowledge

Diagrams can support the steps in procedural texts. Explain how to make hamburgers, illustrating each step with a detailed diagram. Use clear, concise statements next to each diagram.

1.

_____

_____

2.

_____

_____

3.

_____

_____

4.

_____

_____

5.

_____

_____

6.

Dictionary meanings

1. Use your dictionary to locate the meaning of these words.

   (a) ingredients _____

   (b) medium _____

   (c) minced _____

   (d) extra _____

   (e) greased _____

   (f) absorbent _____

Synonyms are words which have similar meanings.

When writing, it is often useful to be able to select another word with a similar meaning.

For example: *hurried*   *rushed*

               dashed   *sped*

---

2. Write **synonyms** for these words. You may find it helpful to consult a dictionary.

   (a) bun

   (b) large

   (c) bowl

   (d) allow

   (e) extra

   (f) mix

3. **Antonyms** are words which have opposite meanings. Write antonyms for these words.

   (a) all

   (b) in

   (c) equal

   (d) on

   (e) add

   (f) heat

4. Give two words that you associate with the given word; for example, smile – grin, happy

(a) hamburger _____   (b) food _____

_____   _____

(c) kitchen _____   (d) microwave _____

_____   _____

(e) vegetables _____   (f) hunger _____

_____   _____

(g) meat _____   (h) chop _____

_____   _____

Find the names

5. Join the groups of letters to find children's names. Use each group once. HINTS: There are three boys and three girls. Look for the capitals!

An	Ro	Ja
Ph	il	ne
ni	an	la
St	ge	ce
ip	rt	be
Di	ev	en

The boys names are _____

_____

_____

The girls names are _____

_____

_____

Syllables

A syllable is a part of a word with one vowel sound. Words may have one or more syllables.

For example: sauce – one syllable

carrot – two syllables

hamburger – three syllables

Breaking words into syllables is a helpful spelling strategy.

1. Count the syllables in these words from the procedure. Clapping the parts may be helpful.

   (a) potato ☐   (b) parsley ☐

   (c) cucumber ☐   (d) absorbent ☐

   (e) salad ☐   (f) flatten ☐

   (g) ingredients ☐   (h) tablespoon ☐

Separating syllables

• Most syllables begin with a consonant.

   For example: to/ma/to

• If there are double consonants, separate them.

   For example: flat/ten

• If there are two consonants together, separate them.

   For example: tab/le

• When there is a base word separate between it and the other syllables.

   For example: melt/ing

2. Syllabify these words. The first one has been done.

   (a) car/rot   (b) c u c u m b e r

   (c) a b s o r b e n t   (d) i n g r e d i e n t s

   (e) m i n c e d   (f) l e t t u c e

   (g) b e e t r o o t   (h) e x t r a

Suffixes are groups of letters attached to the end of a word.

For example: **er**   **est**   **ing**   **ed**   **ful**   **ly**   **ern**

There are many rules for adding a suffix, but usually it is just added to the word. (**Rule 1**)

For example: talk**er**   great**est**   walk**ing**   jump**ed**   wonder**ful**

               like**ly**   north**ern**

Study these rules for adding suffixes.

Rule 2:

When adding a suffix beginning with a vowel to a word ending with a silent **e**, drop the **e**.

For example: grate   grater

               halve   halving

The rhyme '**e** goes away when **ing** comes to stay' is often used to remember part of this rule.

Rule 3:

The one-one-one rule

When adding the suffixes **er**, **ed**, **est**, **ing** and **y** to words of **one** syllable, with **one** short vowel, followed by **one** consonant, that consonant is doubled.

For example: shop   shopping

               swim   swimmer

               flop   floppy

shop		**one** syllable
swim	have	**one** short vowel
flop		**one** final consonant

3.   Use the rule indicated to add the suffixes in brackets to these words.

(a)   Rule 1:   (b)   Rule 2:

     (i)   melt (ing) _____   (i)   manage (ing) _____

     (ii)   quick (ly) _____   (ii)   mince (ing) _____

     (iii)   delight (ful) _____   (iii)   believe (ing) _____

     (iv)   south (ern) _____   (iv)   announce (ing) _____

(c)   Rule 3:

     (i)   chop (er) _____   (ii)   shut (ing) _____

     (iii)   flip (ed) _____   (iv)   fun (y) _____

---

4. Apply the rules to add suffixes to these words.

(a) flavour (ing) (ed)

(b) inhale (er) (ing)

(c) prepare (ing) (ed)

(d) care (ful) (less)

(e) entertain (ment) (er)

(f) slap (ing) (ed)

(g) wonder (ful) (ment)

(h) bright (er) (est)

(i) drum (ing) (er)

(j) pig (y) (let)

5. Circle the correct spelling in each sentence.

(a) The girl playing centre kept (droping, dropping) the ball.

(b) Sarah was standing (faceing, facing) the class.

(c) Mum (scrubed, scrubbed) his football shorts trying to get them clean.

(d) They were (saveing, saving) money for a trip to Austria.

(e) Dad had to drive carefully because the road was very (slipery, slippery).

(f) Our doctor is a very (caring, careing) man.

Verbs

Verbs are the most important words in sentences, in fact a sentence must have at least one verb to be a sentence.

There are many different types of verbs including:

Doing verbs

Some verbs describe an action and are called doing or action verbs.

For example: He **cut** the buns in halves.

     She **cooked** the burgers.

Being verbs

Some verbs describe a state or condition and are called being verbs.

For example: The hamburgers **are** delicious.

     The cook **is** busy.

Having verbs

Some verbs describe ownership and are called having verbs.

For example: The cook **has** a sharp knife.

     The hamburgers **have** sauce in them.

Doing verbs

Because procedures tell you how to make or do something, most of the verbs used are **doing verbs**. In procedures most of the doing or action verbs used to tell someone to do something are called **command verbs**.

Command verbs are usually written at the beginning of sentences.

For example: **Close** the door.

1. (a) Find and underline these command verbs in the procedure on page 1.

mix   make

(b) List five more command verbs from the procedure.

2. Write sentences starting with these command verbs.

(a) Stir

(b) Cook

(c) Wash

(d) Boil

(e) Eat

Being verbs

The verb **to be** changes and has different forms depending on **who** or **when**.

Read these:

I am	I was	I will be
he is	he was	he will be
we are	we were	we will be
you are	you were	you will be
they are	they were	they will be
present tense is happening now	**past tense** has already happened	**future tense** will happen later

3. Use a correct form of the verb **to be** to complete each sentence.

(a) Today I _____ making my lunch. (present tense)

(b) We _____ busy cooking yesterday. (past tense)

(c) They _____ still my favourite cakes. (present tense)

(d) I can see that you _____ a very good cook. (future tense)

(e) These hamburgers _____ delicious. (present tense)

(f) Tomorrow we _____ in the kitchen. (future tense)

(g) She _____ the best cook in this family. (past tense)

(h) We _____ washing up after dinner. (future tense)

Having verbs

The verb **to have** changes and has different forms depending on **who** or **when**.

Read these:

I have	I had	I will have
he has	he had	he will have
we have	we had	we will have
you have	you had	you will have
they have	they had	they will have
present tense **is happening now**	**past tense** **has already happened**	**future tense** **will happen later**

4. Use a correct form of the verb **to have** to complete each sentence.

(a) Bill is staying at home because he _____ a cold. (present tense)

(b) I _____ to cook dinner tonight. (future tense)

(c) On my way home I stopped and _____ a drink. (past tense)

(d) They _____ fish for dinner tomorrow. (future tense)

(e) Our old house _____ an electric oven. (past tense)

(f) We _____ coffee before dinner. (future tense)

Verb tense

Tense tells when something **is happening**, **has happened** or **will happen**.

We change the **tense** by changing the verb.

For example:

  I **cook** the dinner   present tense

  I **cooked** the dinner   past tense

The verb **cook** was changed from the present to the past tense by adding the suffix **ed**.

Adding the suffix **ed** is not the only way to change the tense of a verb, as you have seen with the verbs **to be** and **to have**, but it is the most common way.

5. Add the suffix **ed** to the words.

(a) turn _____   (b) watch _____

(c) cook _____   (d) add _____

(e) fill _____   (f) need _____

6. Write a sentence using each of the **ed** words you wrote in Question 5 above.

(a) _____

_____

(b) _____

_____

(c) _____

_____

(d) _____

_____

(e) _____

_____

(f) _____

_____

(g) Are all your sentences in the past tense? _____

7. Rewrite these sentences in the past tense by changing the verbs.

(a) I **watch** television during the holidays.

(b) My father **enjoys** fishing when he **is** on holidays.

(c) They often **tell** us about travelling to Australia.

Text organisation

A procedure has: *A goal*

A list of requirements

Steps to follow

A test to measure success

Language features

A procedure uses: *Short, clear statements*

Command verbs

Present tense

Text organisation

Language features

Goal

A list of requirements

Command verbs

Steps to follow

Test

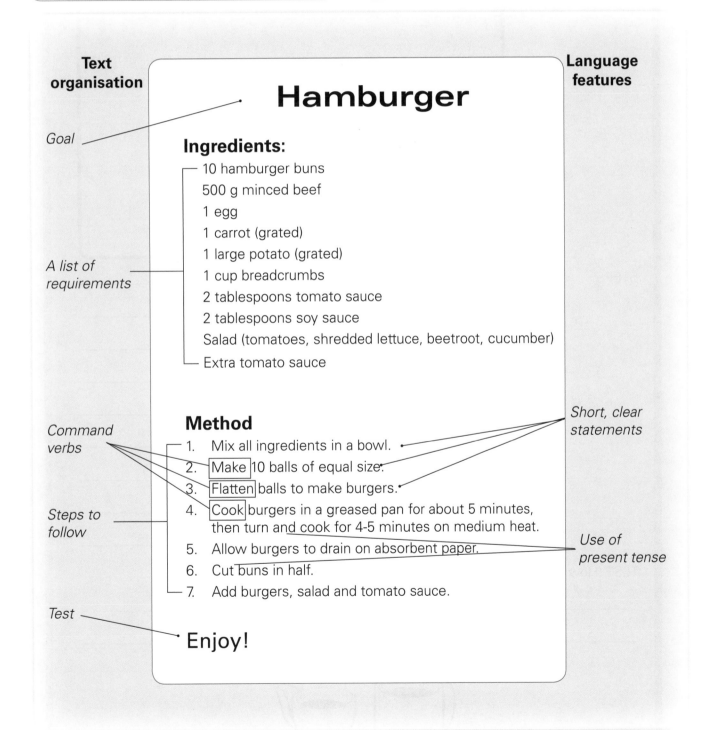

Hamburger

Ingredients:

10 hamburger buns

500 g minced beef

1 egg

1 carrot (grated)

1 large potato (grated)

1 cup breadcrumbs

2 tablespoons tomato sauce

2 tablespoons soy sauce

Salad (tomatoes, shredded lettuce, beetroot, cucumber)

Extra tomato sauce

Method

1.   Mix all ingredients in a bowl.
2.   Make 10 balls of equal size.
3.   Flatten balls to make burgers.
4.   Cook burgers in a greased pan for about 5 minutes, then turn and cook for 4-5 minutes on medium heat.
5.   Allow burgers to drain on absorbent paper.
6.   Cut buns in half.
7.   Add burgers, salad and tomato sauce.

Enjoy!

Short, clear statements

Use of present tense

Write a procedure explaining how you would make a cup of tea or coffee. Use the plan below.

GOAL: _____

REQUIREMENTS:

STEPS: _____

_____

_____

_____

_____

_____

_____

_____

_____

TEST (How would you know if you had been successful?):

_____

_____

Choose one topic from the box. Use the framework to plan your procedure. You may refer to a recipe book; however, you may not copy directly.

How to make:
- a toasted ham and cheese sandwich
- a fruit salad
- your favourite breakfast
- eggs – the way you like them most

TITLE: _____

GOAL: _____

_____

STEPS: _____

_____

_____

_____

_____

_____

_____

_____

_____

_____

_____

_____

_____

_____

_____

EVALUATION (How do you know if you have been successful?):

_____

_____

_____

After you have written the procedure, use the checklist below to edit and proofread your work.

You will self-edit for:

Spelling   Punctuation

Grammar   Sentence structure

You will use a peer editor to check for:

Clear instructions and sense

Checklist

Title of the procedure: _____

1. Does your procedure make sense to you? .... ○ **yes** ○ **no**

2. Did you include a goal? .... ○ **yes** ○ **no**

3. Did you list the things you needed? .... ○ **yes** ○ **no**

4. Have you included all the steps in the correct order? .... ○ **yes** ○ **no**

5. Did you add a test to check that the procedure works? .... ○ **yes** ○ **no**

6. Have you corrected any spelling errors?

   (a)   Did you check that your words look right? .... ○ **yes** ○ **no**

   (c)   Did you use a dictionary? .... ○ **yes** ○ **no**

   (d)   Did you ask someone? .... ○ **yes** ○ **no**

7. Have you used command verbs? .... ○ **yes** ○ **no**

8. Are your statements short and clear? .... ○ **yes** ○ **no**

9. Does each sentence make sense when you read it on its own? .... ○ **yes** ○ **no**

10. Do your statements all start with a capital letter and end with a full stop? .... ○ **yes** ○ **no**

11. Ask a partner to read your procedure.
    Did he/she find it easy to understand? .... ○ **yes** ○ **no**

1. Choose a topic from the box and plan then write a procedure on a separate sheet of paper.

> How to make   • a hot dog   • a boiled egg
>   • a chicken and salad roll   • a cup of hot chocolate

2.

Text:

A procedure has a goal, a list of

_____, steps to

follow and a _____

at the end.

Language:

A procedure uses short, _____

_____ statements

_____ verbs and the

_____ tense.

3. Answer the questions about procedures.

(a) What does the goal tell you? _____

_____

(b) Why are requirements important? _____

_____

(c) Usually the order of the steps is important. Why?

_____

_____

(d) How do you know if a procedure has been followed correctly?

_____

_____

4. (a) Synonyms are words which have _____

For example: _____ and _____

(b) Antonyms are words which have _____

For example _____ and _____

5. Count the syllables in these words.

(a) hamburger   ☐   (b) potato   ☐   (c) size   ☐

(d) tomato   ☐   (e) carrot   ☐   (f) lettuce   ☐

(g) minute   ☐   (h) pan   ☐   (i) dish   ☐

6. (a) A suffix is added to the _____ of a word.

    (b) Add the two suffixes to each word.

    (i)   quick (ly) (er)

    (ii) delight (ed) (ful)

    (iii) flip (ed) (er)

    (iv) believe (ing) (er)

    (v)   shake (er) (ing)

    (vi) shut (ing) (er)

7. Read and underline the verbs.

    (a) Cut the hamburger in half.

    (b) The cook will mix the ingredients.

    (c) Mum bought hamburgers from the supermarket.

    (d) He is busy in the kitchen.

    (e) She has a sharp knife.

8. Underline the verbs in these sentences. Are they in the present, future or past tense? Write your answers on the lines provided.

    (a) She will eat hamburgers for lunch.

    (b) Cut the onion in half.

    (c) The cook shredded the carrot.

    (d) Wash the dishes.

    (e) Drain the lettuce.

    (f) Mum is at home.

    (g) I stopped at the supermarket.

    (h) I will cook dinner.

    (i) He will have the salad.

    (j) The chef added the salt.

Big Rat Island

A recount is a retelling of past events in time order.
Recounts can be written in the form of a diary, a letter or a newspaper article.

Read the following **recount**.

Big Rat Island
Geraldton 6530
Australia

4 August 2013

Dear Ben,

I hope that you're enjoying the school holidays as much as I am. I love Australia, and am having an amazing time. When Mum told me that we would be spending two weeks with her friend, Julia, on Big Rat Island, I didn't know what to think, but it has been great.

We left Perth early to drive north to Geraldton. It took us six endless, boring hours driving through the same flat, uninteresting country. It didn't take us long to find Julia's cousin Val's house, where we left our car. Val drove us to the port and we saw a really cool helicopter. The pilot took the two very small bags we were permitted, loaded them and helped us to climb in and fasten our seatbelts.

The flight was amazing. One minute we were on the ground and then we wobbled up, hovered and flew forwards. It was so noisy, but I enjoyed every minute and there was so much to see. There was even the wreck of an old Dutch sailing ship. Coming in to land was a bit scary, but the pilot landed gently beside the schoolhouse where Julia and Geoff live.

There have been interesting things to do every day. If I want to get up really early, before dawn, I can go out with Geoff, a crayfisherman, on his boat. But I don't go every day.

We often take the dinghy over to a small sandy island close by, because there it is possible to swim and snorkel from the beach. There are thousands of brightly coloured fish and other creatures to see underwater. I even saw a giant cod. The shells are fantastic and many are still alive so we are careful not to injure them.

It has been the best holiday and I can't wait to show you all the photos.

Your friend, Shane

Partner activity

1. Long journeys can become monotonous and boring. What are some of the things you've done or could try to do to fill in time on a long trip? Working with a partner, compile a list of suitable activities. Discuss each activity suggested and decide on the forms of travel for which it is suited and how many participants are needed.

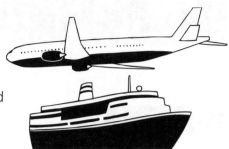

One has been done.

Activity	Forms of travel	People needed
reading	car, train, plane, boat	1

Class activity

What are some of the factors that would contribute to making a journey interesting and enjoyable? Discuss this and record your ideas. Try to be creative!

2. Describe one idea you would like to try.

_____

_____

Structure of a recount

Structure

A recount has:

A title: **What** the recount is about

A setting: **Who** the recount is about

                Where the events happened

                When the events happened

                Why the events happened

The events: **What** events happened

                Events are told in the order in which they happened.

                Each major event is written in a new paragraph.

An ending/Comment: What the writer **thinks** about the events

Read the **recount** about Shane's holiday again. Answer the questions.

Title

What is the recount about? _____

Setting

Who went to Big Rat Island? _____

Who did they visit? _____

When did they go? _____

Where did they go? _____

Why did they go? _____

Events

1. How did they get to Geraldton? _____

_____

2. Where did they go in Geraldton? _____

_____

3. How did they get to the helicopter? _____

_____

4. What did Shane think of the flight?

_____

5. Where did they land? _____

_____

6. Where did they stay? _____

_____

7. What did they do there? _____

_____

Comment

What did Shane think about his holiday?

Reading for information

True or false? Colour the correct answer.

1. Shane and his mother each took a small bag to the island. .... ◯ **true** ◯ **false**

2. There were three people in the helicopter. .... ◯ **true** ◯ **false**

3. There are lovely sandy beaches on Big Rat Island. .... ◯ **true** ◯ **false**

4. Geoff is a teacher. .... ◯ **true** ◯ **false**

5. There are many fish in the water around Big Rat Island. .... ◯ **true** ◯ **false**

Reading for understanding

Use complete sentences to explain your answers to these questions.

1. Was there a limit on the amount of luggage they were allowed to take on the helicopter?

   _____ Why? _____

   _____

2. (a) Where did the helicopter take off from? _____

   (b) Why do you think they used helicopters instead of fixed-wing aircraft?

3. (a) At what time did the crayboats go out? _____

   (b) Why do you think they went out at this time? _____

   _____

4. The water around Big Rat Island is very clear and clean. What information given in the story would make the reader think this?

Applying your knowledge

1. The crayfishing season is limited to just over four months in some places like Big Rat Island. There are also limits on the number of pots each boat can operate.

   Why do you think these rules apply? _____

   _____

   _____

2. Crayfish are delivered to the factory alive.

    Research   (a)   Why do they need to still be alive? _____

    _____

    (b)   How do the crayfishermen keep them alive? _____

    _____

    (c)   Which country buys most of Australia's crayfish? _____

    _____

    (d)   What is another name for crayfish?   _____

    (e)   What colour are raw crayfish?   _____

    (f)   What colour are cooked crayfish?   _____

3. There is a Little Rat Island as well as a Big Rat Island. Suggest a reason for these names.

    _____

    _____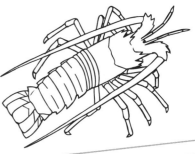

    _____

    _____

Vocabulary

Synonyms

Synonyms are words which have similar meanings.

1. Join the pairs of **synonyms**. One has been done.

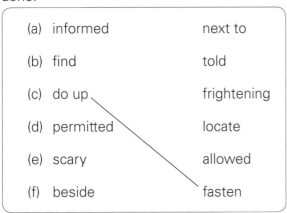

(a)	informed	next to
(b)	find	told
(c)	do up	frightening
(d)	permitted	locate
(e)	scary	allowed
(f)	beside	fasten

Antonyms

Antonyms are words which have opposite meanings.

2. Join the pairs of **antonyms**.

(a)	many	bring
(b)	boring	worst
(c)	take	late
(d)	best	quiet
(e)	early	interesting
(f)	forward	few
(g)	noisy	old
(h)	new	backward

Anagrams are new words formed by changing the order of the letters in words.

For example: form – from

3. Unjumble these words from the recount.

(a) rckwe

(b) gidnyh

(c) knorsel

(d) lpiot

4. (a) Use the clues to find **anagrams** of these words. The first one has been done.

Words	Clues	Anagrams					
FRINGE	A digit on our hand	*f*	*i*	*n*	*g*	*e*	*r*
TURNER	To come back						
SUNLIT	To abuse verbally, affront						
NEARED	Made money						
DENIAL	Attached by hammering						
REPAID	American name for nappy						

(b) The initial letters of the anagrams made the word. _____

5. Use words from the recount *Big Rat Island* to complete the crossword.

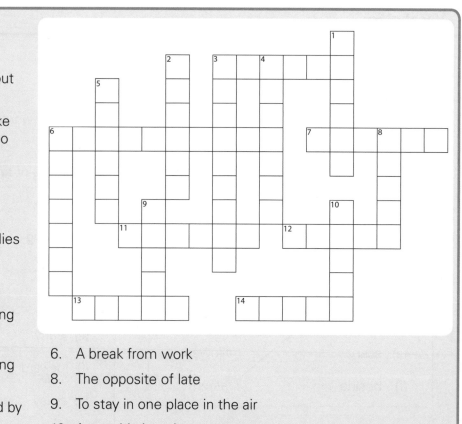

Across

3. Secure

6. An aircraft without fixed wings

7. Someone you like who likes you too

11. Your uncle's son

12. Loud

13. Frightening

14. Someone who flies

Down

1. Hurt

2. A place of learning

3. Wonderful

4. Used for breathing underwater

5. Land surrounded by water

6. A break from work

8. The opposite of late

9. To stay in one place in the air

10. A very big imaginary creature

Word wheel

6. (a) Use the clues given below to find the missing words. Write each word in the word wheel starting from the outside. The first one has been done.

   Note: All the words end with the letter T.

Clues:	1.	An outlaw
	2.	An animal with six legs
	3.	A helpful tool
	4.	An animal like a hare
	5.	To take into police custody
	6.	A special ability or aptitude
	7.	To spend money hoping to make money
	8.	To begin to shoot (plant)
	9.	An insect similar to a cricket or cicada
	10.	To kidnap
	11.	A small lump of precious metal
	12.	To beat or overcome

   (b) The initial letters of each word name a place. What is it? _____

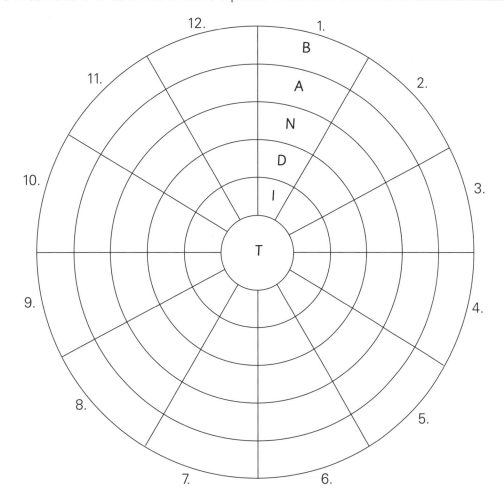

Long and short vowels

Twenty-one letters of the alphabet are called **consonants** and the rest are called **vowels**.

How many vowels are there? _____

Can you say the names of the vowels? Try.

We usually say them in the order in which they are placed in the alphabet.

When we **say** the **names of** the **vowels** in the alphabet, we make a **long** vowel sound.

For example:

acorn   h**e**   k**i**nd   g**o**   t**u**be

1. Read these words with short vowel sounds. Underline the vowels.

   (a) s a n d   (b) b e n t   (c) f i n

   (d) t o p   (e) c u t

2. Read these words aloud and listen for the vowel sound. Is it long or short? Circle all the words with short vowel sounds.

gentle	flight	cray
eat	head	spend
hope	know	climb
belts	wreck	weeks

3. There are many different ways to represent the long **a** sound. Read these words aloud.

gate	stay	stain
eight	lady	rein
reign	prey	

   (a) Write down all the different ways long **a** is represented in these words.

(b) There are other ways to represent long **a**. Try to find some more.

   _____

   _____

   Did you notice that sometimes a long **a** sound was represented by:

   one vowel?   l**a**dy

   more than one vowel?   st**ai**n

   vowels and consonants?   **eigh**t

4. There are many different ways to represent the long **i** sound.

   For example:

i	ie	igh	i–e	y

   Write one word using each different long **i**.

5. Write a word with a long **o** sound to complete each sentence.

   (a) He shoots with a _____ and arrow.

   (b) If you water the flower it will _____.

   (c) A bee stung the boy on his big _____.

   (d) You can _____ when the lights are green.

   (e) They went fishing in their _____.

   (f) The dog was chewing his _____.

   (g) I have a very sore th_____.

6. (a) Underline the long **u** sounds in this sentence.

   > The cute new girl will have to make room to glue these pages into her book.

   (b) List the different ways the long **u** sound was represented.

   _____

   _____

   _____

   _____

7. Choose the correct long **e** sound to complete these sentences.

e	ea	ee	y	ey	i

   (a) The teacher told the boy not to ch_____t by looking at this friend's work.

   (b) Wool comes from sh_____p.

   (c) The film was really funn_____ and made me laugh.

   (d) I lost the k_____ to the door.

   (e) She gave an ice-cream to Belinda and m_____.

   (f) We learnt how to watersk_____.

Newspaper search

You will need a highlighter and a page from a newspaper.

8. (a) Your task is to highlight as many long vowel words as possible in 10 minutes.

   (b) List all the **different ways** of representing each long vowel sound in the table below.

Different ways of representing long vowel sounds	
a	
e	
i	
o	
u	

   (c) Which vowel sound did you find the most of? _____

   (d) Which vowel sound did you find the most different ways of writing? _____

Nouns

> Nouns are naming words. They can name people, places or things.
>
> For example: pilot, island, boat

One simple way to establish if a word is a noun in a sentence is to try to say **a**, **the** or **some** in front of the word in that sentence.

For example:

The pilot flew the helicopter to the island with passengers on board.

The nouns are pilot, helicopter, island and passengers. You could say: **the pilot**, **the helicopter**, **the island** and **some passengers**.

Noun or verb?

Sometimes the same word can be used as a noun in one sentence and a verb (a doing word) in another sentence.

Read these sentences:

Sentence 1   We **left** Perth early.

Sentence 2   In Australia, cars are driven on the **left**.

In Sentence 1 **left** is a verb; that is a *doing* word (We left).

In Sentence 2 **left** is a noun; that is a *naming* word (on the left).

1. Read each sentence and decide if the highlighted word is a noun. (Make sure that you can say **a**, **the** or **some** in front of the word.) Write yes or no on the line.

   (a) I **think** snorkelling is great fun. _____   (b) Have a **think** before you decide. _____

   (c) We went for a long **drive**. _____   (d) He can **drive** the car very fast. _____

   (e) The boys **fish** here every day. _____   (f) They caught some big **fish**. _____

2. Write a sentence using each word as a **noun**. Remember, you need to be able to say **a**, **the** or **some** in front of the word.

   | walk | wreck | swim | holiday |

   (a)

   (b)

   (c)

   (d)

Proper nouns

A **proper noun** is the name of a particular person, animal, place or thing.

For example: Andrew, April, London, Fluffy, Toyota

1. Read the **proper nouns** and write them in the correct categories. Don't forget the capital letters.

Africa	Mars	Mercedes	Saturday	Hitler
February	Europe	Japan	Nile	Rome
Tuesday	Ganges	April	Volvo	Atlantic
Tokyo	Pacific	Germany	Earth	Cleopatra

(a) countries _____ (b) rivers _____

(c) months _____ (d) days _____

(e) cars _____ (f) continents _____

(g) planets _____ (h) cities _____

(i) people _____ (j) oceans _____

2. Write the sentences using capital letters for the proper nouns.

(a) My grandparents will be flying to canada next thursday.

(b) They will be staying in singapore until saturday at the highlight hotel in orchard road.

(c) My aunty sue and her daughter, sarah, are going to meet them and they'll fly to vancouver together.

(d) They will fly across the pacific ocean to los angeles in america where they'll visit disneyland.

Conjunctions

Conjunctions are joining words. They are used to join words and sentences.

For example: Jack **and** Jill (The conjunction is joining two words.)

He fell **and** broke his crown. (The conjunction is joining the sentences. He fell. He broke his crown.)

Three commonly used conjunctions are **and**, **or** and **but**.

3. Use words from the box to complete these well-known sayings which use common conjunctions.

sound	less	later	die	only
dried	bone	go	good	out

(a) sooner or _____

(b) the one and _____

(c) cut and _____

(d) touch and _____

(e) more or _____

(f) skin and _____

(g) do or _____

(h) safe and _____

(i) old but _____

(j) in and _____

4. Underline the conjunctions in these sentences.

(a) Crayfish are expensive because their numbers are limited.

(b) Shane saw many interesting creatures while he was snorkelling.

(c) Shane had a really great time although he hadn't expected to enjoy his holiday.

(d) He felt a bit scared when the helicopter came in and landed.

5. Rewrite the sentences above, changing the word order to start with the conjunctions.

(a) _____

_____

(b) _____

_____

(c) _____

_____

(d) _____

_____

Introductory sentences

Introductory sentences are very important in most writing.

They try to capture the reader's attention. They also provide the setting and often tell the reader **who**, **where**, **when** and **why** something happened.

Read the beginning of the recount *Big Rat Island*.

> I hope that you're enjoying your school holidays as much as I am. I love Australia, and am having an amazing time. When Mum told me that we would be spending two weeks with her friend, Julia, on Big Rat Island, I didn't know what to think, but it has been great.

| **Who**? | the writer (Shane), Mum and Julia | **When**? | school holidays (August) |
| **Where**? | Big Rat Island | **Why**? | To stay on the island |

The title of the recount also helps to capture the reader's attention and gives a clue as to what the recount is about.

Write the introductory sentences of a recount using the information below.

Try to capture the reader's attention by hinting that something interesting happens and by selecting a suitable title. Remember, there is no need to tell WHAT happens (the events), just start the recount.

| **Who**? | My family | **When**? | In winter |
| **Where**? | On a boat | **Why**? | To rescue people |

Title: _____

_____
_____
_____
_____
_____
_____
_____
_____
_____
_____
_____

Choose a suitable topic from the box. Use the plan below, then write your recount in full on a separate sheet of paper.

- *My holiday to ...*   • *Having fun*

- *Swimming (fishing, snorkelling, skiing or parasailing) on my holiday*

- *Catching the ferry (helicopter, aeroplane or ship)*

Title:

Setting: Who

When

Where

Why

Events: 1.

2.

3.

4.

Concluding statement or comment:

After you have written your recount, edit and proofread your work using the checklist below.

Checklist

Title: _____

1. **Setting**:

   Does your recount tell:

   - who was there? .... ○ **yes** ○ **no**

   - where they were? .... ○ **yes** ○ **no**

   - when it happened? .... ○ **yes** ○ **no**

   - why it happened? .... ○ **yes** ○ **no**

2. **Events**:

   Were the events written in the correct order? .... ○ **yes** ○ **no**

3. **Conclusion**:

   Did your recount finish with a concluding comment? .... ○ **yes** ○ **no**

   You will also need to check:

4. **Spelling**:

   - Have you corrected any mistakes? .... ○ **yes** ○ **no**

   - Have you used a dictionary or thesaurus? .... ○ **yes** ○ **no**

5. **Grammar**:

   - Have you used capital letters correctly? .... ○ **yes** ○ **no**

   - Have you used correct punctuation?
     (full stops, commas, apostrophes) .... ○ **yes** ○ **no**

6. Ask a partner to read your recount.

   - Did he/she understand your recount? .... ○ **yes** ○ **no**

   - Did your partner correct any errors? .... ○ **yes** ○ **no**

   - Partner's name _____

1. Choose a topic from the box below and plan, then write a recount in full on a separate sheet of paper. Use the editing and proofreading chart as a guide to check your work.

> *Riding my bike (scooter)*   *Playing in a team*
>
> *Going to the zoo*   *My visit to _____*   *An adventure*

2. Structure of a recount

   The TITLE tells [   ]

   The [   ] tells who, what, [   ]

   when and why.

   The events tell [   ] happens and are told in [   ]

   Recounts finish with [   ]

3. Synonyms are words which have

   [   ] meanings.

   Circle the word which is the matching synonym.

(a)	enemy	friend / foe
(b)	tired	weary / active
(c)	scared	afraid / happy
(d)	stay	stop / exit
(e)	slender	round / thin
(f)	halt	begin / cease
(g)	vacant	empty / full
(h)	adult	child / grown-up
(i)	fat	skinny / obese
(j)	question	ask / answer

4. Antonyms are words which have

   [   ] meanings.

   Circle the word which is an antonym.

(a)	wrong	right / false
(b)	full	round / empty
(c)	answer	question / wrong
(d)	brave	scared / happy
(e)	front	exit / back
(f)	large	huge / small
(g)	wet	dry / baked
(h)	smooth	rough / shiny
(i)	forget	answer / remember
(j)	kind	laugh / nasty

5. Read these words and listen for the vowel sounds. Are they long or short? Put an **L** (long) or an **S** (short) next to each word.

    (a) tight _____   (b) gain _____   (c) obese _____

    (d) loss _____   (e) extend _____   (f) chase _____

    (g) give _____   (h) scatter _____   (i) hospital _____

    (j) shutter _____   (k) scope _____   (l) flute _____

    (m) sheep _____   (n) brave _____   (o) shiny _____

6. (a) Nouns are _____ words for people, _____

        and _____.

    (b) Verbs are _____ words.

    (c) Write three nouns. _____

    (d) Write three verbs. _____

In some sentences, the same word can be a noun or a verb.

7. Read these sentences. Is the highlighted word a noun or a verb?

    (a) It was a long **drive** to the coast.

    (b) Ben can **drive** the car very fast around the track.

    (c) The fisherman did not catch any **fish** today.

    (d) Dad did not want to **fish** today.

    (e) The girls went for a **swim** in the bay.

    (f) He can **swim** across the river.

8. Circle the proper nouns.

Saturday	flower	running	April	shower	Jill
Sydney	Mercedes	France	aeroplane	walking	Everest
Timothy	New York	jumping	laughing	Thames	Monday
Alfa Romeo	India	Pluto	hopping	Napoleon	Churchill
Singapore	Michael Caine	fairy	Nicole Kidman	swinging	library
Spain	Japan	ship	house	November	difficult

9. Write a proper noun for these categories.

    (a) country _____   (b) month   _____

    (c) day   _____   (d) person _____

    (e) car   _____   (f) planet _____

    (g) river   _____   (h) city   _____

    (i) ocean   _____   (j) continent _____

10. Write the sentences, using capital letters for the proper nouns.

    (a) My sister, emily, enjoyed reading the book, black beauty.

    _____

    (b) The rocky mountains stretch down the west coast of canada and the united states of
        america.

    _____

    _____

11. Underline the conjunction in each sentence.

    (a) Jack lost his wallet while he was on holiday.

    (b) You won't do well in your exams if you don't study.

    (c) I'll take my raincoat because it's raining.

    (d) When it's cold and wet, Dad drives his car to work.

12. Rewrite the sentences above, changing the word order to start with the conjunction.

    (a) _____

    _____

    (b) _____

    _____

    (c) _____

    _____

    (d) _____

    _____

Skateboard menace

Expositions analyse, interpret and evaluate the environment around us. Their purpose is to persuade by presenting one side of an argument.

Read the **exposition**.

Skateboard menace

As a senior citizen I wish to record my strong objections to the menace presented by skateboarders to people using footpaths, parks and even shopping centres. They must be banned!

I regularly need to take evasive action as I walk my dog along the path surrounding Weston Park. My eyesight, hearing and reactions are no longer good and I am often unaware of the danger of being bowled over until it is upon me. I find this frightening, much to the delight of the skateboarders, who seem to enjoy my discomfort and find it amusing. Is this fair?

I know that there are signs prohibiting skateboards in shopping centres, but these are ignored by the skateboarders and not enforced by the centre staff.

Parents need to take more responsibility for the whereabouts of their children. Surely there are better and safer things for the young people to be doing!

It is high time that our footpaths become available for all to use safely. I urge people to make their opinions known to our local council and have skateboards banned. Then these bans must be rigorously enforced by the authorities.

Ken Smith

Partner activity

1. The writer is obviously very angry.

    Discuss, then make a list of the things that made the writer angry.

    _____

    _____

    _____

    _____

    Do you think the writer's comments are fair? _____

Class activity

2. Writers often reveal a great deal about themselves when they write.

    What does the reader know about the writer?

    Brainstorm and list information in the letter under the headings: FACTS   and   OPINIONS

    Does everyone agree about the **facts**, or are some of them really just opinions?

    Look at the **opinions**. Place them in order, starting with the one most people agree with through to those that are most in dispute.

    Discuss the evidence provided in the text and whether, as readers, you were influenced by what you know and think about skateboards and older people.

Structure of an exposition

Structure

An exposition uses persuasive language to present a particular point of view.
This exposition has:

A title:	Tells what the exposition is about.
An overview:	Briefly tells what the writer thinks about the subject.
Reasons:	Arguments to persuade people, in order of importance.
Conclusion:	Final comment and summing up.

Read *Skateboard menace* again.

Answer these questions:

Title

What is the exposition about? _____

_____

Overview

What does the writer think should happen? _____

_____

Reasons or arguments

1. Why doesn't the writer know when skateboarders are approaching?

    _____

    _____

2. Why can't the writer get out of the skateboarders' way? _____

    _____

3. What do the skateboarders do when they see they have frightened the writer?

    _____

    _____

4. Why don't skateboarders take any notice of signs in shopping centres? _____

    _____

5. What does the writer think parents should do? _____

    _____

Conclusion

What does the writer want people to do? _____

_____

WORKING WITH THE TEXT   **Reading**

Reading for information

True or false? Colour the correct answer.

1. The writer has a dog.   ○ **true** ○ **false**

2. Skateboarders worry the writer because he can't hear them coming.   ○ **true** ○ **false**

3. The shopping centre needs to put up signs banning skateboards.   ○ **true** ○ **false**

4. The writer is frightened that the skateboarders might knock him over.   ○ **true** ○ **false**

5. The writer doesn't like skateboards because they are noisy.   ○ **true** ○ **false**

Reading for understanding

1. Do you think the writer is more angry or frightened? _____

   Explain why you think this. _____

   _____

   _____

   _____

2. Do you think the writer likes children?

   Give two reasons.

   • _____

   • _____

3. What does the writer want parents to do?

   _____

   _____

   _____

Applying your knowledge

(a) What do you think shopping centres could do to stop skateboarders skating inside the centres?

   _____

   _____

   _____

   _____

(b) List some other things that children do that could upset older people.

   _____

   _____

   _____

   _____

(c) List some things that children could do to help older people or make them happy.

   _____

   _____

   _____

Synonyms

Synonyms are words with the same or similar meanings.

You may need to use a dictionary or a thesaurus to match synonyms for these words used in the exposition.

1. Join the synonyms. One has been done for you.

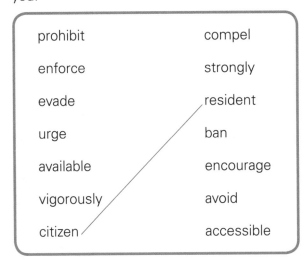

prohibit	compel
enforce	strongly
evade	resident
urge	ban
available	encourage
vigorously	avoid
citizen	accessible

Compound words

Compound words are words made from two or more smaller words.

For example: tooth + paste = toothpaste

2. Join two of these words to make compound words found in the exposition.

skate	path	eye
where	be	up
on	boarder	sight
came	abouts	foot

_____ _____

_____ _____

_____ _____

3. Write a compound word using each of these words either at the beginning or end of the word.

day	over	out	ship

_____ _____

_____ _____

4. (a) Join the groups of letters to form occupations. Use each group once.

la	ct	nt	er
st	te	wy	ist
do	de	ar	or
ach	au	ti	er
th	rse	nu	or

(b) Write the occupations in alphabetical order.

_____

_____

_____

_____

_____

_____

_____

_____

The occupations are la_____, do_____,

de_____, te_____, ar_____,

au_____ and nu_____.

Masculine, feminine or neutral

In the past many occupations were restricted to either males or females and masculine or feminine nouns were used.

For example: policeman

Today we use neutral words that can mean either feminine or masculine because men and women do the same job.

For example: police officer

5. Can these nouns be used to name only masculine, only feminie or both? Write M, F or MF after each.

(a) dentist ☐   (b) nurse ☐

(c) pilot ☐   (d) salesman ☐

(e) waitress ☐   (f) housemaid ☐

(g) postman ☐   (h) teacher ☐

(i) chairperson ☐   (j) sales assistant ☐

(k) principal ☐   (l) headmistress ☐

(m) artist ☐   (n) ballerina ☐

6. Complete this table.

	Masculine	**Feminine**	**Neutral**
(a)		queen	monarch
(b)			child
(c)			grandparent
(d)	father	mother	
(e)	brother		sibling
(f)		daughter	offspring
(g)	husband		
(h)		mare	horse
(i)	boar		pig

Vowel sounds

In English the vowel sounds can be written in many different ways. This makes spelling quite a challenge. Look at the long vowel sounds in these words.

Vowel sound	
a	b**a**by, pl**ay**, r**ai**n, sh**a**ve, r**ei**gn, th**ey**, **eigh**t
e	tr**ee**, sh**e**, ch**ea**t, monk**ey**, pon**y**, Soph**ie**, th**e**se, sk**i**, f**oe**tus
i	f**i**nd, h**i**de, t**ie**, br**igh**t, cr**y**, h**eigh**t, **ei**ther
o	g**o**, gr**ow**, t**oe**, th**ough**, b**oa**t, cha**u**ffeur
u	bl**ue**, st**ew**, c**u**te, em**u**

There are more ways to write these vowel sounds, but many of the common ones are listed above.

Try to add to these lists.

The simplest way to know which spelling to use is to write it and see if it looks right.

1. Circle the spelling that looks right.

(a) ceiling   ceeling   (b) receipt   recept

(c) donkey   donky   (d) recieve   receive

(e) feerce   fierce   (f) caffene   caffeine

Spelling hints

2. Check that you understand these generalisations. They are not rules, but they are generally true. Find an example for each one and write it on the line provided.

(a) Final **e** sound

The **e** sound at the end of a word is often **y** or **ey**.

_____

_____

> **Note:**
> **y** is more common.
> **ey** often follows the letter k.

(b) Middle **e** sound

The **e** sound in the middle of a word is often **ee** or **ea**.

_____

_____

> **Note:**
> **ea** is often used in food we **ea**t.
> For example; p**ea**s, b**ea**ns
> **ea** is also used in **ea**r and h**ea**r

(c) Middle **a** sound

The **a** sound in the middle of a word is often **ai** or **a–e**. In words ending with **tion**, **a** is used.

_____

_____

_____

(d) Final **a** sound

The **a** sound at the end of a word is often **ay**.

_____

> **Hint:**
>
> **a** is used in **ation** words such as **station** and **separation**

(e) Final **i** sound

The **i** sound at the end of a word is often **y**.

_____

(f) Middle **i** sound

The **i** sound in the middle of a word is often **i–e**. Words ending with **t** often use **igh**.

_____

_____

> **Hint/Note:**
>
> **igh** is often used before **t** such as in **light**, **bright**

(g) Final **o** sound

The **o** sound at the end of a word is often **ow** or **o**.

_____

_____

> **Note:**
>
> **o** is used in small words such as **go** and **no**

(h) Middle **o** sound

The **o** sound in the middle of a word is often **oa** or **o–e**.

_____

_____

_____

_____

(i) Final **u** sound

The **u** sound at the end of a word is often **ue** or **ew**.

_____

_____

Class activity

3. There are exceptions to the generalisations above. Find an exception for each.

(a) [_____]   (b) [_____]   (c) [_____]

(d) [_____]   (e) [_____]   (f) [_____]

(g) [_____]   (h) [_____]   (i) [_____]

All or Al?

The word **all** is always spelt **all**, but when it is used in a compound word it is spelt **al**.

For example: **al**ready

4. Add **al** to write compound words using:

so	together	most	mighty	ways	though

(a) _____   (b) _____

(c) _____   (d) _____

(e) _____   (f) _____

The most common spelling error involving **all** is **all right**.

This is difficult because it is not always understood that **all right**, unlike the words you have just written, is NOT a compound word. It is in fact two separate words and so the word **all** remains unchanged.

All sorts is not a compound word, but two separate words (except for licorice allsorts).

always	already	all right	all sorts	also

5. Write a sentence using each of the words in the box above.

- _____
  _____

- _____
  _____

- _____
  _____

- _____
  _____

- _____
  _____

Emotive language

Expositions use language that tries to affect the way people think and feel.

Read these two sentences:

The **man** walked down the road.

The **burglar** walked down the road.

Words like **man**, **woman** or **child** are colourless, neutral words and when we hear or read them nothing definite comes to our minds and we don't have any strong feelings. But other words like **burglar**, **coward** or **hero** affect our feelings and we could feel a bit frightened, worried or happy.

1. Read these words and decide if they would be good ones to use in an exposition because they affect people's feelings or emotions. Decide if they are emotive or neutral.

Emotive words	Neutral words
burglar	man

ugly   large   murder

small   rich   careful

neglectful   disgusting   quiet

monster   sensational

2. Rewrite these neutral sentences to make them more emotive. Try to create a sense of fear by adding words and changing the words with bold text. The first one has been done for you.

(a) I **saw** a **man walking** through the park.

> I stared at a desperate robber sneaking through the dark, deserted park.

(b) The **large** animal **called out** as it **went** into the cave.

(c) The **man came** into the bank and **asked** for some money.

3. Rewrite these emotive sentences in more neutral language. The first one has been done for you.

   (a) The lightning flashed, the thunder roared and the rain pelted down.

   > There was thunder, lightning and heavy rain.

   (b) The piercing screams of the terrified child attracted everyone's attention.

   (c) The hero plunged into the raging water to rescue the drowning, terrified dog.

   (d) The brilliant doctor saved the life of the desperately ill patient by giving him life-saving antibiotics.

Punctuation

Punctuation is an important part of writing and allows the writer to communicate thoughts and ideas clearly.

1. Read *Skateboard menace* again.

   (a) Use a highlighter to mark all the capital letters. Check that you understand why each one is a capital.

   (b) Highlight the full stops (.), question marks (?) and exclamation marks (!). Check that you understand why the writer has used them.

   (c) Highlight all the commas.

2. (a) Capital letters are used at the start of sentences. Write two words from the text with capitals because they start sentences.

   _____ and _____

   (b) Capital letters are used for names of people and places. Find two examples from the text.

   _____ and _____

   (c) Question marks indicate questions. Write a question from the text.

   _____

(d) Write a sentence from the text, ending with an exclamation mark.

_____

(e) How many commas did you find? _____

(f) How many commas are used in lists? _____

(g) How many commas are used to indicate where the reader should pause? _____

Apostrophes for possession

Apostrophes can be used to indicate ownership.

For example: the boy's skateboard   The skateboard belongs to the boy.

the old man's coat   The coat belongs to the old man.

Notice that the apostrophe is placed directly after the owner. (The tail of the apostrophe 'points' to the owner.)

If there is more than one owner the apostrophe is still placed after the owners, but it looks quite different.

For example: the bees' hive   The hive belonging to the bees.

the teachers' books   The books belonging to the teachers.

3. Circle the owner or owners in each of these. Remember, the apostrophe is placed after the owner or owners.

(a) the officers' helmets   (b) some puppies' tails

(c) a girl's basket   (d) my friend's bike

(e) the class's work   (f) many children's books

(g) the ladies' knitting   (h) the bird's nest

Apostrophes can indicate different meanings.

Read these:

the umpire's decisions means one umpire

the umpires' decisions means more than one umpire

my friend's party means one friend

my friends' party means more than one friend

4. Write singular (s) or plural (p) after each of these:

    (a) the tigers' tails ☐   (b) the actor's costumes ☐

    (c) the roof's tiles ☐   (d) the teachers' books ☐

    (e) the horses' stables ☐   (f) the plane's engines ☐

    (g) the children's pets ☐   (h) the tables' legs ☐

    (i) the computer's keyboard ☐   (j) the cars' tyres ☐

    (k) the bands' members ☐   (l) the truck's load ☐

5. Write these using an apostrophe to show ownership.

    (a) the treasure belonging to the pirates

    _____

    (b) the people belonging to the nation

    _____

    (c) the photographs belonging to my grandmother

    _____

    (d) the edge of the water

    _____

    (e) the badges belonging to some police officers

    _____

    (f) the castle belonging to Count Dracula

    _____

    (g) the ties belonging to the gentlemen

    _____

    (h) the towels belonging to the swimmers

    _____

    (i) the make-up belonging to the girls

    _____

Emotive language

Expositions use emotive language because writers wish to affect the way people think and feel.

1. Rewrite these neutral sentences using more emotive language to create the feelings nominated at the end of the sentences.

    For example:

    > The man walked along the path.   fear

    The big, ugly, scarfaced man strode menacingly down the path towards me.

    (a) | He looked out the window. | cold

    _____

    _____

    _____

    _____

    (b) | She walked along the sand. | heat

    _____

    _____

    _____

    _____

    (c) | They sat looking at the trees. | peace

    _____

    _____

    _____

    _____

    (d) | His father was cross. | anger

    _____

    _____

    _____

    _____

Titles

Titles are important. They should explain or at least give a clue as to what a piece of writing is about.

A good title is the first chance a writer has to capture the reader's attention.

A good title:
- attracts attention
- relates to the topic
- explains the topic, usually using up to six words
- is easy to remember.

2. (a) Rate the title *Skateboard menace* on these four criteria using the scale:

   1–poor   2–fair   3–good   4–very good   5–excellent.

   (i) attracts attention   ☐   (ii) relates to the topic   ☐

   (iii) uses fewer than six words to explain a topic   ☐   (iv) is easy to remember   ☐

   (b) Suggest two different titles for the exposition.

   _____

   _____

3. Read the emotive language descriptions you used in Question 1 and write two suitable titles for each.

   For example:

   > The big, ugly, scarfaced man strode menacingly down the path towards me.
   >
   > Possible titles: Scarface
   >
   >   Held for ransom

   Possible titles:

   (a) _____

   _____

   (b) _____

   _____

   (c) _____

   _____

   (d) _____

   _____

Plan an exposition. It may be in the form of an essay or a letter. Choose a title from the box below. Use the plan to organise your ideas, then write your exposition in full on a separate sheet of paper. Use persuasive language.

- **Good manners**
- **Older people**
- **Noise pollution**
- **Safety in parks**

TITLE:

INTRODUCTORY STATEMENT:

(What do you believe?)

ARGUMENTS:

(Thoughts and ideas which support what you believe)

CONCLUSION:

(Link your ideas together to form a final comment which summarises your position.)

After you have written your exposition, use the following checklist to edit and proofread your work.

You will self-edit for:

Spelling   Punctuation
Grammar   Sentence structure

Ask a peer to edit your work to check the persuasive language and that your arguments are sequenced from the most persuasive to the least.

Checklist

Title of exposition: _____

1. Do you understand an exposition's purpose? .... ◯ **yes** ◯ **no**

2. Does your exposition:

    • clearly state a problem in the introduction? .... ◯ **yes** ◯ **no**

    • provide background information? .... ◯ **yes** ◯ **no**

    • list reasons to support your belief or view? .... ◯ **yes** ◯ **no**

    • use facts to support arguments? .... ◯ **yes** ◯ **no**
      (diagrams, photographs, facts and figures)

    • sequence arguments from strongest to weakest? .... ◯ **yes** ◯ **no**

    • include a final paragraph which reinforces and
      summarises main points?. .... ◯ **yes** ◯ **no**

3. Have you used persuasive words? .... ◯ **yes** ◯ **no**

4. Ask your partner to read your exposition.

    • Did s/he understand your point of view?................................... ◯ **yes** ◯ **no**

    • Did it make sense?... ◯ **yes** ◯ **no**

    • Were you able to persuade your partner to agree with your
      point of view? .... ◯ **yes** ◯ **no**

1. Choose a topic from the box and plan, then write, an exposition in full on a separate sheet of paper. The exposition may be in the form of a letter or an essay.

> • **Showing consideration** • **Dogs in parks** • **Park facilities**

2. Complete the following.

   Expositions are written to

   _____

   others to think or do something.

   Structure of an exposition

   An exposition has:

   • a title   • _____

   • _____   • _____

3. Complete these statements about expositions.

   (a) The title tells _____

   (b) The overview tells what the writer _____

   _____

   (c) The _____ are the arguments which try to persuade the audience.

   (d) The conclusion is the _____

   _____

4. Synonyms are words with the _____ meaning.

5. Write compound words using one of these words either at the beginning or the end of the word.

   > self   in   tooth   cream

   _____   _____   _____   _____

6. Write two words with different ways of making the:

   'a' sound   [   ]   [   ]

   'e' sound   [   ]   [   ]

   'i' sound   [   ]   [   ]

   'o' sound   [   ]   [   ]

   'u' sound   [   ]   [   ]

7. Write these words in the correct category.

Emotive	Neutral

ran	glared
neglected	walked
looked	roared
took	grabbed
saw	snatched

8. Punctuate these sentences.

    (a) my skateboard was stolen last friday but I think I know who took it.

    (b) during the july holidays I hope to go horse riding canoeing skating and sleep over at ben wilson's house

9. Write singular (s) or plural (p) after each of these:

    (a) the **sheep's** coat ☐　　　　(b) the **schools'** concert ☐

    (c) the **bags'** contents ☐　　　　(d) the **table's** legs ☐

    (e) the **birds'** nest ☐　　　　(f) the **crocodile's** teeth ☐

10. Write these using an apostrophe to show ownership.

    (a) the sails belonging to the boats

    _____

    (b) the cows belonging to the farm

    _____

    (c) the bread belonging to the baker

    _____

    (d) the nets belonging to the fishermen

    _____

    (e) the book belonging to the teacher

    _____

Man's best friend

A **narrative** describes a series of events and circumstances often involving fictitious characters.

Read the **narrative**.

Man's best friend

Mr Leake lived in the house next door. We called him Farmer Leake because he used to own a wheat farm. I knew he was very old because he looked like my grandpa, who was 66. Farmer Leake had a dog that was nearly as old as he was. I knew that because the dog walked as slowly as Farmer Leake did. His name was Rupert. He had grey whiskers like Farmer Leake and his eyes were always sad and watery too. Every morning, they would walk their slow walk down the garden path, through the old rusty gate to the corner shop three houses away. There Farmer Leake would buy the daily paper for himself and a treat for Rupert. Every afternoon the pair of them would sit on the front porch in the sun, waving to the kids who lived in the street as they returned home from school. It was their daily routine.

I sometimes wondered if he was lonely, but he never complained. As they walked past, some of the kids would call out funny names or mimic Farmer Leake. They would laugh at his brown cardigan with the missing buttons, or his shirt collar folded under, exposing his hairy neck. If Mum caught us she would tell us off.

'You'll be old one day. Don't be so rude!'

Mum would occasionally cook Farmer Leake a roast and give the bone to Rupert and Dad would mow his lawn.

One day in late autumn, Farmer Leake stopped walking down his path, through the gate to the corner shop. So did Rupert. He stopped sitting on the porch in the afternoon. So did Rupert. And he stopped waving to the children.

Nobody noticed.

One morning, just as the first light was peeking through the curtains, I heard a dog barking. I listened for a while, but it stopped. Later that day, as I was returning from school I heard it again. Barking, continuously. It was then I realised that I hadn't seen Farmer Leake and Rupert for several days. I dropped my school bag by the door and jumped the low fence that separated the two houses. Tentatively I approached Farmer Leake's front door. The barking was louder now. I rang the bell, but there was no sound. Like the rest of the house it was in need of repair. I banged on the old wooden frame. I waited. The only sound was my own heart thumping in my chest. There was no answer, so I called out.

'Mr Leake, are you there?'

I looked through the window, my hands cupped against the reflection of the afternoon sun. I couldn't see; the curtains were closed. The barking started again, so I called out.

'It's all right Rupert, old boy. I'm coming to get you.'

I ran down the side of the house and up the back stairs, two at a time. I tried the doorknob, but it was locked. Gathering some strength and momentum, I threw the full weight of my body against the door. The bolt gave way and before I knew it, I was inside.

'Rupert!' I called. He responded with a whimper. I followed the sound and opened the door of Mr Leake's bedroom.

'Rupert! Are you there, boy?' I called, more quietly now, frightened of what I might find. At first I couldn't see anything, just the rumpled bed, and then I heard both of them: Rupert whimpering and Farmer Leake weakly calling me.

'Is that you, Ben?'

There on the floor was Farmer Leake, Rupert by his side.

The next day, Mum took me to the hospital. A photographer from the daily newspaper snapped me as I entered the room.

'Is this the hero then?' he asked Farmer Leake.

I protested modestly, 'I didn't do anything. I just followed Rupert's barking and whimpering. Rupert did a wonderful job.'

'He really is a man's best friend', said Farmer Leake.

Class discussion

1. (a) How did the story make you feel?

   (b) Was the ending as you anticipated?

   (c) How do you think Ben felt: • as he approached Farmer Leake's house?

      • after his photo appeared in the paper?

2. (a) What neighbourly acts did Ben's family do for Farmer Leake?

   (b) Brainstorm some other good neighbourly acts.

   (c) Why is it important to look after neighbours?

Partner activity

3. List some adjectives that could be used to describe Rupert.

4. Give your partner a detailed description of Farmer Leake.

   Remember to tell about his appearance, personality and actions.

5. (a) Make up a dialogue between Ben and Farmer Leake after Ben entered the house.

   (b) Take turns at playing both characters.

Structure of a narrative

A narrative has:

A title: Indicates what the story is about
Gets the attention of the reader

Orientation: *Who* Main character(s) and possibly minor characters are introduced

What Initiating event that starts the story

Where The setting or location

When Time the story takes place

Complication: The problem which involves the main character

Resolution: How the problem is solved

Conclusion: What happened in the end

Read the narrative *Man's best friend* and answer the questions.

TITLE

(a) Is *Man's best friend* a suitable title for this story? _____

(b) Why do you think this? _____

_____

ORIENTATION

WHO

(a) What are the names of the main characters
     in the story?

_____

_____

_____

(b) Name two minor characters in the story.

_____

_____

WHERE Where does this story take place?

_____

WHEN When did it happen?

_____

_____

WHAT Name three things that Farmer Leake
          did every day.

_____

_____

_____

_____

_____

COMPLICATION

(a) What happened in late autumn?

_____

_____

(b) What had happened to Farmer Leake? _____

RESOLUTION

How did Ben help? _____

_____

CONCLUSION

Why did Farmer Leake refer to Rupert as 'a man's best friend'? _____

_____

Reading for information

Fill in the missing words from the story.

1. Farmer Leake used to own a _____ farm.

2. The corner shop was _____ houses away.

3. Every day he bought a _____ paper for himself and a _____ for Rupert.

4. Farmer Leake wore a _____ cardigan with _____ buttons.

5. A _____ fence separated the two houses.

6. Farmer Leake was taken to _____.

Reading for understanding

1. Were Ben's parents good neighbours?

   ◯ **yes** ◯ **no**

   Why do you think this? _____

   _____

   _____

2. Was Rupert a useful pet for an old man?

   ◯ **yes** ◯ **no**

   Why do you think so? _____

   _____

   _____

3. Why was Ben's mother annoyed?

   _____

   _____

   _____

4. Why did Ben think that Farmer Leake was old?

   _____

   _____

   _____

Applying your knowledge

1. Make a list of things dogs do to be called 'man's best friend'.

   _____

   _____

   _____

   _____

   _____

2. What are some ways in which you could help your neighbours?

   _____

   _____

   _____

   _____

   _____

3. Ben became a 'hero'. Name someone you consider to be a 'hero' and give reasons why you think this.

   _____

   _____

   _____

   _____

Word snakes

1. (a) Create a word snake using only nouns (naming words) from the story. Try to make it as long as you can. Ask a partner to separate the words.

    For example:

    handsshopeyesstairssunnewspaperroutine

    [   ]

    (b) Now try the same exercise using only verbs (doing words).

    [   ]

Synonyms for very

The word **very** is often overused in writing.

There are many more precise words to use which convey meaning and interest readers.

    For example: **very** old – ancient

                    very cold – freezing

---

2. Find one word with the same or similar meaning to the following:

(a) very hot [   ]   (b) very big [   ]

(c) very small [   ]   (d) very tired [   ]

(e) very smart [   ]   (f) very angry [   ]

(g) very long [   ]   (h) very rich [   ]

(i) very thin [   ]   (j) very fast [   ]

3. Replace the word **very** to give a similar meaning.

   For example: **very** cold – **bitterly** cold

   (a) very hot _____ hot
   (b) very big _____ big

   (c) very small _____ small
   (d) very tired _____ tired

   (e) very smart _____ smart
   (f) very angry _____ angry

   (g) very long _____ long
   (h) very rich _____ rich

   (i) very poor _____ poor
   (j) very fast _____ fast

Alliteration

Alliteration is the use of the same sound at the beginnings of words.

For example: **b**usy, **b**uzzing **b**ees

slippery, **s**limy **s**nakes

It is often used to gain attention and add interest to writing.

---

4. Make up your own alliteration to describe each of these.

   (a) _____ , _____ farmer

   (b) _____ , _____ house

   (c) _____ , _____ whiskers

   (d) _____ , _____ cardigan

   (e) _____ , _____ barking

   (f) _____ , _____ curtains

   (g) _____ , _____ reflection

   (h) _____ , _____ buttons

   (i) _____ , _____ photograph

   (j) _____ , _____ school

1. Find words in the story using these clues. Make sure to spell them correctly.

   (a) a garment which keeps you warm

   c __ __ __ __ __ __ n

   (b) another word for sometimes

   o __ __ __ __ __ __ __ __ __ y

   (c) ongoing or unceasingly

   c __ __ __ __ __ __ __ __ __ y

   (d) answered or replied

   r __ __ __ __ __ __ __ d

   (e) hesitantly, cautiously, uncertainly

   t __ __ __ __ __ __ __ __ __ y

   (f) driving power or strength

   m __ __ __ __ __ __ m

2. Use a dictionary to help you to find these words and spell them correctly.

   (a) a person who is in hospital   pat __ __ __ __

   (b) what we use to propel a bike   ped __ __ __

   (c) widely favoured or admired   pop __ __ __ __

   (d) to hire or lease transportation   cha __ __ __ __

   (e) a flat piece of wood or plastic used to mix paints on   pal __ __ __ __

   (f) spoken or written with ease   flu __ __ __

   (g) resulting in death   fat __ __

   (h) away, as from a place or country   for __ __ __ __

   (i) the choice of roads taken to get to a place   rou __ __

Confused words

3. Some words look or sound alike and are easily confused. Underline the correct words. You may use a dictionary.

   (a) The president spoke (fluent, fluid) English to the (forth, fourth) annual meeting.

   (b) The new team captain was (formally, formerly) (excepted, accepted) by the manager and members.

   (c) The (patent, patient) was transferred to hospital after the (fateful, fatal) accident.

   (d) The (palate, palette) was an (effective, affective) way for the artist to mix his paints.

   (e) A (charted, chartered) boat was a (popular, poplar) way to see around the reef.

   (f) The cyclists (peddled, pedalled) along the (rout, route) through the village.

Adjectives

Adjectives are words used to describe people, places and things; their appearance, personality and function.

For example: the **stooped**, **wizened**, **grey-haired**, **friendly**, **old** man

the **warm**, **comfortable**, **knitted**, **brown** cardigan

1. Choose two adjectives to describe each of these nouns.

(a) [   ] , [   ] neighbour

(b) [   ] , [   ] cottage

(c) [   ] , [   ] dog

(d) [   ] , [   ] boy

(e) [   ] , [   ] wheelbarrow

2. How many of the adjectives you wrote described:

(a) appearance? [   ]   (b) personality? [   ]   (c) function? [   ]

Advertisement

3. (a) Write an advertisement to sell your bike.

Remember to give information about its appearance, how it functions and its special features. The more detailed information you provide, the more likely you are to sell it.

FOR SALE

(b) Highlight or underline the adjectives in your advertisement.

Adding adjectives

4. (a) Rewrite this short passage adding appropriate adjectives to the highlighted nouns. Remember to use commas if you add more than one adjective.

> The **dog** barked when he heard the **truck** stop outside the **house**. He wagged his **tail** when he realised that the **driver** was his **owner**.

_____

_____

_____

_____

_____

_____

_____

(b) How many adjectives did you add? _____

(c) How did the adjectives change the passage? _____

_____

_____

(d) How many of the adjectives you wrote describe:

appearance? ☐   personality? ☐   function? ☐

Punctuation

Commas

Commas are used to separate items on a list. They are NOT needed before the word **and** in a list.

5. Use commas to separate the nouns in these sentences.

(a) He picked up his hat shoes socks cricket bat and ball and raced out the door.

(b) The farmer's wife fed the chickens ducks pigs goats and the geese down by the pond.

(c) Zac grabbed his surfboard hat flippers and shirt and raced towards the waves.

6. Use commas to separate the **adjectives** in these sentences.

(a) Some excited energetic hot noisy children dived into the cool clear refreshing blue water.

(b) The worried young girl looked sadly at her faded torn blue jeans.

(c) The puppy chewed the beautiful white expensive new sports shoe he had found under Jessica's bed.

(d) The shiny black stylish extremely fast motorbike thundered down the quiet street.

7. Use commas to separate the **verbs** in these sentences.

(a) The dog jumped twisted turned stretched and caught the ball.

(b) Fortunately the footballer regained his feet after tripping falling rolling and grabbing his ankle.

(c) The dancers were twisting turning swirling and gliding gracefully across the floor.

(d) The wild cat arched its back hissed spat and retreated into the bush.

Commas are also used when we need a pause in a sentence to make it easier to understand.

For example:

Before you go to sleep tonight, remember to set your alarm clock.

8. Add commas to these sentences.

(a) Snatching the old lady's bag the robber raced off down the street.

(b) Hoping to find her lost dog Wendy searched in all the neighbours' gardens.

(c) Waiting patiently the dog sat near the gate.

(d) Trying to avoid a collision the driver slammed on his brakes and swerved to the left.

Titles

The purpose of a title is to explain what a piece of writing is about and to capture the reader's attention.

A good title   1. attracts attention

2. relates to the topic

3. explains the topic, usually using up to six words

4. is easy to remember.

Read these passages and write a title for each.

Title

The three boys dug frantically to uncover more of the old box Ben had stubbed his toe on while he was chasing the cricket balls way down the beach.

'I wonder what's in it?' queried Peter as he scooped up sand and threw it behind him.

'It could be a pirate's chest', answered Ben and he winked at his friend, Todd.

'Probably is', replied Todd, 'and full of treasure I bet', he continued.

Peter danced around the older boys, his eyes as big as saucers.

Finally, they had excavated sufficient sand to prise open the lid and three pairs of eyes stared in disbelief.

Title

Sun shining – sky shimmering

Wind whispering, clouds creeping and

shadows shivering

Daybreak dawning, magnificent morning

River rippling, boats bobbing

Seagulls soaring, cormorants calling and

pelicans preening, magnificent morning

Down by the river

Where boys will be building

Waves are washing and dogs are digging

Day breaking, magnificent morning

Title

Mrs Harris needed a hat. She went to Mr Martin the milliner early on Monday morning. Mr Martin smiled. He lifted a straw hat from the counter. It had a big red flower on it. Mrs Harris tried it on.

'Oh no, this will not do', she said.

Mr Martin reached up to the next shelf and lifted down a felt hat. It was orange and had a big blue bow at the back. Mrs Harris tried it on.

'Oh no, this will not do', she said.

Mr Martin got his stepladder. He reached for the top shelf and lifted down a hatbox. It had been there a long time and was very dusty on top. He opened the lid and lifted out a black hat. It was covered in feathers that swayed gently as Mr Martin handed it to Mrs Harris. She looked underneath and then she looked on top of it. She put it on. She smiled at Mr Martin.

'This will do very nicely, thank you.'

---

2. (a) Do you think *Man's best friend* is an appropriate title for the narrative? ◯ **yes** ◯ **no**

    (b) Did it attract your attention? ◯ **yes** ◯ **no**

    (c) Does it relate to the topic? ◯ **yes** ◯ **no**

    (d) Does it explain the topic? ◯ **yes** ◯ **no**

    (e) Is it easy to remember? ◯ **yes** ◯ **no**

    (f) Choose an alternative title for the story. Make sure your title fits the above criteria.

    _____

A narrative = characters + complication + resolution

Characters: Effective writers make their characters appear real by describing their appearance, personality and likely actions.

Complication: The problems facing the main characters are outlined.

Resolution: The resolution must develop from the situation confronting the main character(s), be believable and relate to the personality of the characters involved.

Characters

3. Use the grid below to record information about the main characters in the narrative.

Character	Appearance	Personality	Actions
Farmer Leake			
Ben	boy, young	caring, friendly, helpful	broke down door, found Farmer Leake, got help
Rupert			

4. (a) Who do you think is the hero in this story? _____

    (b) Why? _____

    _____

    (c) What other character in the narrative could be considered a hero? _____

Writing resolutions

- Resolutions that are satisfying to the reader must develop out of the situation confronting the main character(s).

- The action taken must also relate to the personality of the characters involved.

- Stories can have two possible endings.

    1. The ending the reader HOPES will happen (... and the woodcutter saved Little Red Riding Hood).

    2. The ending the reader FEARS will happen (... and the wolf ate Little Red Riding Hood).

Tips for writing resolutions

DO	**DON'T**
1. Make certain the main character works out the solution.	1. Depend on coincidence to solve the problem. (Bill just 'finds' a gun in his pocket.)
2. Create suspense by keeping the characters from reaching their goal too easily or quickly.	2. Introduce a new character to save the day.
3. Create additional difficulties. That is, have more than one attempt to solve the problem.	3. Have the main character announce 'And then I woke from a dream.'

5. Answer these questions about the resolution in *Man's best friend*.

    (a) Was the ending what you hoped or feared would happen?   ◯ **yes** ◯ **no**

    (b) Did the main character work out the solution?   ◯ **yes** ◯ **no**

    (c) Was there some suspense?   ◯ **yes** ◯ **no**

    (d) Did the main character reach his goal too easily and quickly?   ◯ **yes** ◯ **no**

    (e) Was there more than one attempt to solve the problem?   ◯ **yes** ◯ **no**

    (f) Was the resolution just a strange coincidence, unrelated to the story?   ◯ **yes** ◯ **no**

    (g) Was a new character introduced to save the day?   ◯ **yes** ◯ **no**

    (h) Was it all a dream?   ◯ **yes** ◯ **no**

    (i) Did the actions taken relate to the personalities of the character involved?   ◯ **yes** ◯ **no**

    (j) (i) Was the resolution satisfying to you?   ◯ **yes** ◯ **no**

        (ii) Explain your answer. _____

        _____

        _____

A narrative has:

A title:	Indicates what the story is about
	Gets the attention of the reader
Orientation:	*Who* Main character(s) and possibly minor characters are introduced
	What Initiating event that starts the story
	Where The setting or location
	When Time the story takes place
Complication:	The problem which involves the main character
Resolution:	How the problem is solved
Conclusion:	What happened in the end?

Mans best friend has been analysed using a narrative plan. Study this to help you understand the different parts of a narrative.

Title	Man's best friend
ORIENTATION	
• Character	Mr Leake – retired farmer, old, grey-haired, slow, lonely
	Ben – young, caring, friendly, helpful
	Rupert – old, faithful, grey
	Mum and Dad – helpful, neighbourly
• Setting/Location	Residential area
• Time	One day in late autumn
INITIATING EVENT	
• What starts the action?	Ben hears Rupert barking.
• How does this involve the characters?	He wonders what has happened to Farmer Leake.
COMPLICATION	
• What problem do the characters have?	Farmer Leake can't get out of his bedroom.
• What caused the problem?	Farmer Leake was very weak.
RESOLUTION	
• How is the problem solved?	Ben heard Rupert barking, broke in and found Farmer Leake and Rupert.
CONCLUSION	
• What happened in the end?	Farmer Leake went to hospital and Ben was considered the hero by the local press.

1. Use your imagination to complete the narrative plan started for you. Don't forget an appropriate title. The resolution should come naturally from the story.

Title	
ORIENTATION	

Choose your own extra characters.

• Characters	Pet shop owner (Mr Wilson)
	Security officer
	_____
	_____
• Setting/Location	Pet shop
• Time	In the middle of the night

INITIATING EVENT	
• What starts the action?	The security alarm rings.
• How does this involve the characters?	The security firm contacts Mr Wilson.

COMPLICATION	
• What problems do the characters have?	Mr Wilson has to investigate.
• What caused the problem?	_____
	_____

RESOLUTION	
• How is the problem solved?	_____
	_____
	_____

CONCLUSION	
• What happened in the end?	_____
	_____
	_____

Choose a topic from the box below and write a narrative. Use the plan on the next page to guide your ideas.

When you are ready, write the story in full on a separate sheet of paper.

> • *Farm holiday*   • *A true friend*
>
> • *Unlucky*   • *Lost in the woods*

Title	

ORIENTATION

- Characters
  (Appearance, personality,
  likely actions)

- Setting/Location

- Time

INITIATING EVENT

- What event starts the
  action?

- How does this involve the
  characters?

COMPLICATION

- What problems do the
  characters have?

- What caused the problem?

RESOLUTION

- How is the problem solved?

CONCLUSION

- What happened in the end?

When you have completed your story, proofread and edit it using the following questions as a guide.

Checklist

Title: _____

1. Title

(a)   Does the title indicate what the story is about?.............................○ **yes** ○ **no**

(b)   Does it get the attention of the reader? ....○ **yes** ○ **no**

2. Orientation

(a)   Does the beginning draw the reader into the characters' world?....○ **yes** ○ **no**

(b)   Are the characters believable? ....○ **yes** ○ **no**

(c)   Do their actions fit their personalities?...○ **yes** ○ **no**

(d)   Is the setting realistic? ....○ **yes** ○ **no**

3. Initiating event

Is the problem known at the beginning of the story?.........................○ **yes** ○ **no**

4. Complication

Is the problem believable?...○ **yes** ○ **no**

5. Resolution

(a)   Does the resolution fit the complication?.......................................○ **yes** ○ **no**

(b)   Have the problems been solved?..○ **yes** ○ **no**

6. Conclusion

Is the ending satisfying to the reader? ....○ **yes** ○ **no**

7. Punctuation and spelling

Have you checked the following?

(a)   Spelling – use a dictionary or ask someone ....○ **yes** ○ **no**

(b)   Punctuation – including capital letters, full stops,
       question marks, commas and direct speech................................○ **yes** ○ **no**

(c)   Paragraphs for new ideas..○ **yes** ○ **no**

8. Vocabulary

(a)   Have you used some interesting adjectives? ....○ **yes** ○ **no**

(b)   Have you used any compound words? ....○ **yes** ○ **no**

(c)   Have you used more interesting verbs instead of 'said'?...............○ **yes** ○ **no**

1. Choose a title from the box and plan and write a NARRATIVE.

> - ***A difficult neighbour***
> - ***The faithful pet***
> - ***My hero***
> - ***Playground menace***

2. (a) A narrative has five parts which are a t_____, an o_____

   a c_____ a r_____ and a c_____.

   (b) The orientation tells who, _____, _____ and when.

   (c) The resolution tells how the problem is _____.

3. Find **one word** with the same or similar meaning to the following:

   (a) very cold ☐

   (b) very brave ☐

   (c) very sad ☐

   (d) very pretty ☐

4. Replace the word **very** to give a similar meaning.

   (a) very cold _____ cold

   (b) very brave _____ brave

   (c) very sad _____ sad

   (d) very pretty _____ pretty

5. Alliteration is the use of the _____ sound at the beginning of words. Make up your own alliteration using these words.

   (a) ☐ ☐ neighbour

   (b) ☐ ☐ dog

   (c) ☐ ☐ street

   (d) ☐ ☐ flower

6. These words look or sound alike. Circle the correct one.

   (a) The sick (patent, patient) was taken to hospital.

   (b) The team won their (fourth, forth) game of football for the season.

7. Choose two adjectives to describe each of these nouns.

   (a) _____, _____ witch

   (b) _____, _____ bike

   (c) _____, _____ friend

8. Use commas to separate the items in these sentences.

   (a) Mum made the pizzas using cheese ham tomatoes pineapple and olives.

   (b) The old rusted dilapidated timber shed collapsed during the storm.

The *Titanic* mystery

ANALYSIS

Reports give facts clearly without unnecessary information or opinions.

Read this **report** about the ship, *Titanic*.

The *Titanic* mystery

INTRODUCTION

The sinking of RMS *Titanic* on its maiden voyage in 1912 is one of the world's most infamous disasters.

THE SHIP

Titanic was built in Belfast, Northern Ireland. It had a double bottomed hull with sixteen watertight compartments to keep it afloat, even if its hull was breached. A new invention, the wireless radio, had been installed to make it possible for the crew to call for help in an emergency. This large ship carried 1300 passengers and a crew of 890. *Titanic* had four funnels and was powered by coal-fired steam engines.

FACILITIES

Titanic was considered to be the safest ship afloat and the most luxurious. It had four restaurants, a theatre, a Turkish bath, tennis and squash courts, a mini-golf course and a kennel for the passengers' dogs.

THE MAIDEN VOYAGE

Titanic set sail for New York, leaving Southampton on 10 April 1912. The captain, Edward J Smith, was eager to set a new record for the Atlantic crossing. He didn't reduce speed or post extra lookouts, despite warnings he received about icebergs in the sea lanes.

THE DISASTER

On 14 April, at 11.35 pm, 650 kilometres south-east of Newfoundland, a crewman spotted an iceberg. Evasive action was taken immediately, but it was unsuccessful; the ship crashed into the iceberg. One hour later, women and children were ordered to the lifeboats, but because they believed the ship to be unsinkable, many ignored the warning. There hadn't been any lifeboat practice for the crew or the passengers. In the confusion, the crew launched some lifeboats before they were full, despite the fact that there weren't enough lifeboats for all the people on board the ship. The crew radioed for help, but there was no response. *Californian*, a ship that was only 16 kilometres away, didn't hear the signal because a crewman had turned the radio off when he went off duty. Some of the crew saw flares sent up by *Titanic*, but didn't recognise them as distress signals.

One hundred kilometres away, the liner *Carpathia* heard the call and headed for *Titanic*, but arrived two hours after the ship sank at 2.20 am, with the loss of 1500 lives. *Carpathia* took the 700 survivors on to New York.

THE CONSEQUENCES

The White Star Line's owners were found guilty of negligence by the courts because there were only enough lifeboats for one-third of the people on board *Titanic* and the crew had not been properly trained in emergency procedures.

In 1913 the International Convention for Safety of Life at Sea met in London and established the following rules:

1. Ships must have lifeboats for all aboard.

2. Lifeboat drills must be conducted on every voyage.

3. Radios must be kept on and manned 24 hours every day.

An International Ice Patrol was also formed in the North Atlantic shipping lanes.

CONCLUSION

The mystery of why the 'unsinkable' *Titanic* actually sank was finally solved in 1985 by Dr Robert Ballard, who used submersible robots and cameras to locate the wreck four kilometres below the surface. He established that it was not the huge gap in the ship's hull, but that some of the hull's plates had buckled and rivets joining the seams had come loose, flooding the compartments and causing the disaster.

Class activity

1. (a) Discuss the safety features needed on ships.

   (b) Compare and contrast these to the safety features needed on smaller boats.

2. Compile a list of natural disasters and discuss what people should do in each of these situations; for example, a wildfire, an earthquake, a flood.

Partner activity

3. Think of a situation where you have been in danger or 'at risk' (or make one up).

   • Explain the situation and how you acted.

   • Discuss the safety equipment that could have been useful in this situation.

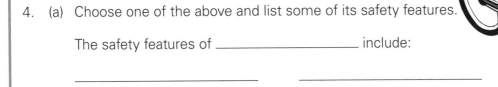

• your bike	• a car
• your home	• your school

4. (a) Choose one of the above and list some of its safety features.

   The safety features of _____ include:

   _____   _____

   _____   _____

   _____   _____

   (b) Describe these safety features to a partner.

Structure of a report

This report has:	A title:	Identifies the subject of the report
	Classification:	Provides information about the focus of the report
	Description:	When it happened
		Where it happened
		What was involved
		How it happened
		Why it happened
		What the consequences were
	Conclusion:	A summary or comment

Read the report *The* Titanic *mystery* and answer the questions.

Title:

(a) What is the title of the report? _____

(b) Is it an appropriate title? _____

Classification

What was *Titanic*? _____

_____

Description

(a) What did *Titanic* look like?

_____

_____

_____

_____

(b) What facilities did it have?

_____

_____

_____

_____

(c) What happened to *Titanic*?

_____

_____

_____

_____

(d) Where did it take place?

_____

_____

_____

_____

(e) When did it happen?

_____

_____

_____

_____

(f) How did the disaster occur?

_____

_____

_____

_____

Conclusion

(a) What were the consequences? _____

_____

(b) When and how was the mystery solved? _____

_____

_____

Reading for information

True or false? Colour the correct answer.

1. *Titanic* had a double-bottomed hull with eighteen watertight
   compartments..○ **true** ○ **false**

2. The captain of *Titanic* wasn't informed there were icebergs in
   the sea lanes..○ **true** ○ **false**

3. The crewman on *Californian* didn't hear the signal for help because
   it wasn't loud enough...○ **true** ○ **false**

4. The 700 survivors were taken to New York on *Carpathia*.................○ **true** ○ **false**

5. The White Star Line's owners were found guilty because there were
   only enough lifeboats for half the people on board *Titanic*. ....○ **true** ○ **false**

Reading for understanding

1. Why was *Titanic* considered to be the safest ship of its time?

2. Why did the captain of *Titanic* not heed the warnings about icebergs?

3. What proved to be the reason *Titanic* sank?

4. Why do you think it was important for the International Convention for Safety of Life at Sea to establish new rules?

Applying your knowledge

Choose eight important events from the report *The* Titanic *mystery* and draw and label them in sequential order.

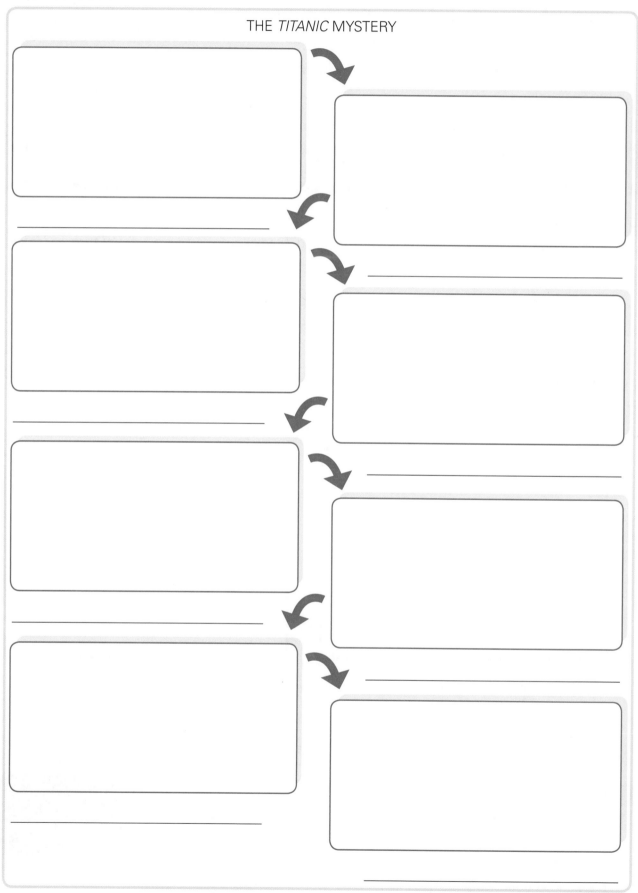

THE *TITANIC* MYSTERY

1. **Hexagon puzzle**

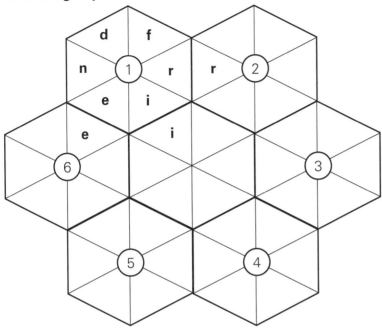

Fill in the spaces in the numbered hexagons above using the given clues. Each answer can start anywhere in the shape but always runs clockwise. Where the hexagons touch, they have the same letter. The first one has been done for you. When you have finished, the letters in the middle hexagon will spell the mystery word.

The mystery word is _____

Clues

1. a mate or pal

   f_____

2. examples are the Nile and the Congo

   r_____

3. to coil again

   r_____

4. they run on rails

   t_____

5. to quit a job

   r_____

6. shredded

   g_____

2. **Word puzzle**

Each box contains a group of three letters from a nine-letter word. Use these groups to answer the clues below. The leftover groups will make another nine-letter word. The first letter of the first group of letters has been provided.

jew	pin	pap	aph
kid	hon	cat	oon
edu	eap	tur	nap
ped	erb	eym	ion
ell	ogr	ise	ery
aut	quo	ack	ple

Clues:

1. A holiday after a wedding

   h_____

2. rings, bracelets, earrings

   j_____

3. A soft-covered book

   p_____

4. We go to school for this

   e_____

5. A personal signature

   a_____

6. a tropical fruit

   p_____

7. taken for ransom

   k_____

The leftover groups make the word

_____

Alphabetical theme list

3. Write a word associated with the ocean starting with each letter of the alphabet. The first one has been done.

(a) aquatic   (b) _____   (c) _____

(d) _____   (e) _____   (f) _____

(g) _____   (h) _____   (i) _____

(j) _____   (k) _____   (l) _____

(m) _____   (n) _____   (o) _____

(p) _____   (q) _____   (r) _____

(s) _____   (t) _____   (u) _____

(v) _____   (w) _____   (x) _____

(y) _____   (z) _____

Acrostic

Acrostics are poems using the first letters of a word to begin words or phrases related to that word.

For example: **S**ailing the oceans
Hauling heavy cargoes
In port unloading
Passengers and cargo
Sailing out to sea

4. You may like to use some of your theme words when you complete this acrostic poem.

T _____

I _____

T _____

A _____

N _____

I _____

C _____

5. Change the first word to the last word in five moves. Only one letter may be changed each time and you must use real words.

(a)

have
side

(b)

mass
line

(c)

side
more

(d)

bale
mine

(e)

fear
sees

(f)

tall
rain

6. Use the groups of two letters in each row to make an animal.

rb	il	ge	(a) _____
ey	nk	mo	(b) _____
ba	er	dg	(c) _____
lr	wa	us	(d) _____
bb	it	ra	(e) _____
fe	et	rr	(f) _____
ja	ar	gu	(g) _____

7. Complete the crossword.

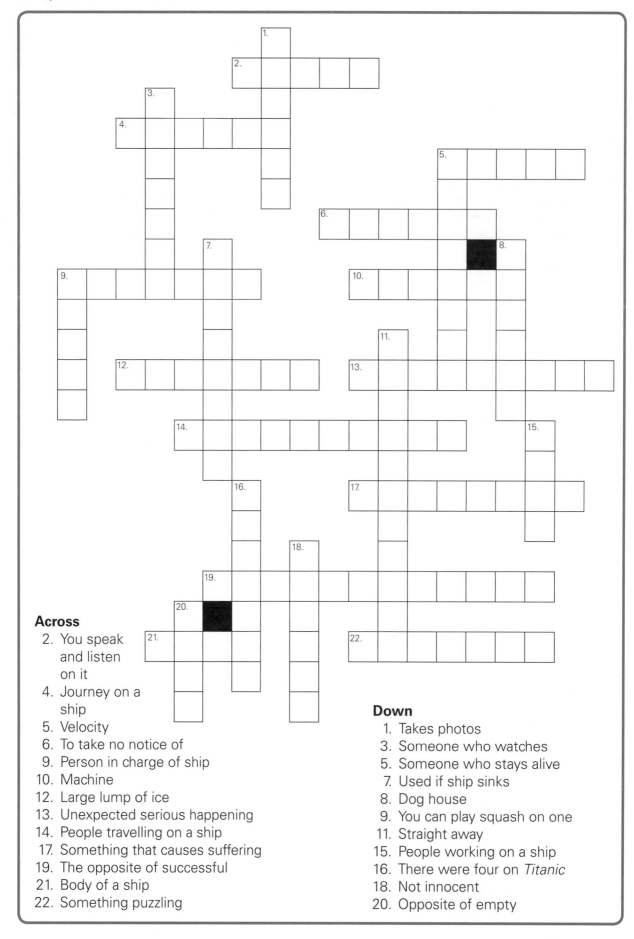

Across

2. You speak and listen on it
4. Journey on a ship
5. Velocity
6. To take no notice of
9. Person in charge of ship
10. Machine
12. Large lump of ice
13. Unexpected serious happening
14. People travelling on a ship
17. Something that causes suffering
19. The opposite of successful
21. Body of a ship
22. Something puzzling

Down

1. Takes photos
3. Someone who watches
5. Someone who stays alive
7. Used if ship sinks
8. Dog house
9. You can play squash on one
11. Straight away
15. People working on a ship
16. There were four on *Titanic*
18. Not innocent
20. Opposite of empty

Plurals

Spelling rule

To change nouns (naming words) from singular (one) to plural (more than one) just add **s** in most words.

For example: biscuit   biscuits

cake   cakes

1. Change these words from singular to plural.

(a) restaurant _____   (b) afternoon _____

(c) funnel _____   (d) voyage _____

(e) lifeboat _____   (f) disaster _____

(g) iceberg _____   (h) minute _____

Spelling rule

To change nouns ending in: **ch**   **sh**   **s**   **x**   **z**   **o**
from singular to plural add **es** because it is often easier to say.

For example: patch   patches   box   boxes

dish   dishes   waltz   waltzes

toss   tosses   potato   potatoes

There are exceptions to this rule including:

words ending with   **oo**   kangaroos, shampoos, cockatoos, zoos

words ending with   **o**   radios, banjos, pianos, sopranos, solos

words ending with   **ch**   monarchs, stomachs
                     Note: In these words **ch** is pronounced with a **k** sound.

2. Change these words from singular to plural.

(a) watch _____   (b) fox _____

(c) dish _____   (d) tomato _____

(e) glass _____   (f) waltz _____

(g) lunch _____   (h) box _____

(i) wish _____   (j) potato _____

(k) class _____   (l) fizz _____

Spelling rule

To change a noun ending in **f** or **fe** change the **f** or **fe** to **v** and add **es**.

For example: calf   calves

                        life   lives

There are exceptions to this rule including:

words ending with   **ff**   sheriffs, staffs, cliffs, puffs, skiffs, staffs

words ending with   **f**   reefs, roofs, waifs, chiefs, handkerchiefs, gulfs

3. Change these words from singular to plural.

    (a) loaf _____ (b) elf _____

    (c) half _____ (d) knife _____

    (e) shelf _____ (f) wife _____

    Remember: If you are unsure, consult a dictionary.

4. Change these words from singular to plural using the different rules above.

    (a) engine _____ (b) match _____

    (c) wolf _____ (d) chief _____

    (e) radio _____ (f) passenger _____

    (g) life _____ (h) class _____

5. Change these words from plural to singular.

    (a) stomachs _____ (b) hives _____

    (c) tomatoes _____ (d) waltzes _____

    (e) buses _____ (f) bosses _____

    (g) knives _____ (h) echoes _____

6. Cross out the incorrect spelling.

    (a) The class (photos, photoes) were taken last Friday.

    (b) There were many (kangaroos, kangarooes) feeding in the paddock near the homestead.

    (c) They say that cats have nine (lifes, lives).

    (d) Many residents decided to add deadlocks to their doors because of the number of (thiefs, thieves) in the area.

    (e) His favourite (sandwichs, sandwiches) are made with peanut butter and jam.

Prepositions

A preposition connects one thing with another showing how they are related.

Prepositions can tell about **place** and **time**.

1. Read these sentences. The highlighted words are **prepositions**. Write **place** or **time** at the end of each sentence.

    (a) They sailed **on** *Titanic*. _____

    (b) The ship hit an iceberg **during** the night. _____

    (c) The crew were not trained properly **before** the journey. _____

    (d) Women and children were allowed to have places **in** the lifeboats. _____

    (e) The ship sank **at** 2.20 am. _____

2. Use a preposition from the box to complete each sentence.

around	while	without	inside	before	through

    (a) The ship sailed _____ enough lifeboats.

    (b) _____ *Titanic* sank it was believed to be unsinkable.

    (c) The crew tried to go _____ the iceberg.

    (d) _____ the ship was sinking, *Californian* was only 10 miles away.

    (e) *Titanic* was sailing _____ cold, dangerous seas.

    (f) The crew launched some lifeboats without enough people

    _____ them.

3. Circle the correct **prepositions**.

    (a) I am afraid (of, at) mice.

    (b) The doctor cared (after, for) her patients.

    (c) The class sat and waited quietly (after, for) their teacher.

    (d) The applicant was well qualified (for, with) the position.

    (e) The dam is full (of, with) water.

    (f) The principal spoke (to, at) the prefects before the assembly.

4. Use each word as a **preposition** in a sentence about ships. Try to make your sentences interesting.

(a) after

(b) between

(c) over

(d) in

(e) with

(f) around

(g) while

(h) outside

5. Circle the **preposition** in each sentence.

(a) The dog doesn't eat until his owner tells him to start.

(b) Our school football team is playing at home this week.

(c) I went windsurfing during the holidays.

(d) My alarm clock didn't work at five o'clock this morning.

(e) My laptop computer is in my bedroom.

(f) Why is that girl sitting under my desk?

(g) Wash your hands before you eat.

(h) We loaded the program onto my computer.

(i) I've been playing cricket since I was six years old.

(j) You can't wear that top with those jeans.

Facts and opinions

Reports present facts (true statements) rather than opinions (what the writer believes).

1. Fact or opinion? Colour the correct answer.

   (a) Icebergs are dangerous. .... ⃝ **fact** ⃝ **opinion**

   (b) Icebergs float. .... ⃝ **fact** ⃝ **opinion**

   (c) *Titanic* hit an iceberg. .... ⃝ **fact** ⃝ **opinion**

   (d) The captain of *Titanic* was careless. .... ⃝ **fact** ⃝ **opinion**

   (e) *Titanic* was unsinkable. .... ⃝ **fact** ⃝ **opinion**

   (f) The Atlantic Ocean is treacherous. .... ⃝ **fact** ⃝ **opinion**

2. Choose one means of transport from the box below.

   Write three FACTS and three OPINIONS about it.

planes	ships	trains	cars
buses	motorcycles	bicycles	trucks

   Facts about

   1. _____

   _____

   2. _____

   _____

   3. _____

   _____

   Opinions about

   1. _____

   _____

   2. _____

   _____

   3. _____

   _____

Reports give facts clearly, without unnecessary information.

Good report writers are able to choose the most relevant or important facts and write them clearly.

3. (a) Read the section *The* Titanic *mystery* again and choose eight important keywords to write below.
Note: The keywords should indicate the most relevant information provided in that section.

Keywords

```
┌──────────┐ ┌──────────┐ ┌──────────┐ ┌──────────┐
└──────────┘ └──────────┘ └──────────┘ └──────────┘
┌──────────┐ ┌──────────┐ ┌──────────┐ ┌──────────┐
└──────────┘ └──────────┘ └──────────┘ └──────────┘
```

(b) Work with a partner to compare keywords and select the four most important ones.

Keywords

```
┌──────────┐ ┌──────────┐
└──────────┘ └──────────┘
┌──────────┐ ┌──────────┐
└──────────┘ └──────────┘
```

(c) Write the four facts you consider to be the most important in this section, using your four keywords.

1. _____

   _____

2. _____

   _____

3. _____

   _____

4. _____

   _____

Writing a report

Choose a topic for a report from the box below and use the plan to prepare it, then write it in full on a separate sheet of paper.

Remember to use facts NOT opinions.

You may need to research to find relevant information.

Earthquake	*Flood*	*Wildfire*	*Tsunami*

Title:

Classification: (type) _____

_____

Description:

Appearance

Location

Time

Causes

Effects

Other important facts

Comment/conclusion _____

_____

_____

After you have written your report in full, use the checklist below to edit and proofread your work.

You will self-edit for:

Spelling   Punctuation

Grammar   Sentence structure

You will use a peer editor to:

Check sense

Ensure that you have written facts

Checklist

Title of report: _____

1. Does your report describe:

    (a) appearance? .... ⚪ **yes** ⚪ **no**

    (b) location? .... ⚪ **yes** ⚪ **no**

    (c) time? .... ⚪ **yes** ⚪ **no**

    (d) causes? .... ⚪ **yes** ⚪ **no**

    (e) effects? .... ⚪ **yes** ⚪ **no**

    (f) any other facts? .... ⚪ **yes** ⚪ **no**

2. Have you written facts, not opinions? .... ⚪ **yes** ⚪ **no**

3. Do you have a concluding statement? .... ⚪ **yes** ⚪ **no**

4. Have you corrected any spelling errors? .... ⚪ **yes** ⚪ **no**

5. Have you used capital letters and full stops correctly? .... ⚪ **yes** ⚪ **no**

6. Did your peer editor:

    (a) understand your report? .... ⚪ **yes** ⚪ **no**

    (b) believe your facts are true? .... ⚪ **yes** ⚪ **no**

1. Choose a topic from the box below and write a report. Use a report plan to organise your ideas before writing the report in full on a separate sheet of paper.

| cyclone | an accident |
| lightning | drought |

2. Reports should give facts not

_____ and

should not provide unnecessary

_____ .

3. Write the plurals of these words:

(a) dish _____ (b) church _____

(c) house _____ (d) box _____

(e) friend _____ (f) tomato _____

(g) radio _____ (h) knife _____

(i) glass _____ (j) loaf _____

4. Cross out the incorrect words.

(a) Chips are made from (potatos/potatoes).

(b) Please sweep up all the (leafs/leaves) from the patio.

(c) The children enjoyed (sandwiches/sandwichs) for lunch.

(d) The music shop was selling (pianoes/pianos) at a reduced price.

(e) My father collects antique (watchs/watches).

5. Circle the correct prepositions.

(a) The class was studying books (of/about) disasters.

(b) The kettle is full (with/of) water.

(c) A football champion spoke (to/at) the school assembly.

(d) The boss was very pleased (at/with) the work and the attitude (to/of) the new apprentice.

(e) The hairdresser did her best to care (for/of) her clients.

6. Use each word as a **preposition** in a sentence about rivers.

(a) over _____

(b) beside _____

(c) into _____

(d) after _____

7. Circle the **preposition** in each sentence.

(a) The ship sailed to the Pacific Islands.

(b) The crew had to board the ship 24 hours before sailing.

(c) I enjoy reading books about science fiction.

(d) Please sit at the table until everyone has finished eating.

(e) He dived into the cool, clear water.

(f) May I watch television until 9 o'clock?

Wooden spoon puppet

The purpose of a procedure is to **direct**, **inform** or
explain how to do something.

Read the instructions for making a wooden spoon puppet.

Wooden spoon puppet

Puppets can be made from all sorts of materials. Wooden spoons are suitable because they are just the right shape to make a head and body.

REQUIREMENTS:
- Wooden spoon
- Assorted coloured paints
- Paintbrush
- Pencil, ruler
- Fabric
- Scissors
- Needle and thread
- Strong non-toxic glue
- Scraps of ribbon, wool

STEPS:

1. Paint the round part of the spoon the colour of skin.

2. When dry, draw nose, eyes and mouth and then paint them.

3. Cut a piece of fabric as long as the spoon handle and 30 cm wide.

4. Sew two lines of running stitches along the top edge.

5. Pull these threads to gather.

6. Knot the threads together.

7. Glue the gathered edge around the spoon handle.

8. Glue a scrap of ribbon around the gathering to hide it.

9. Add any additional decorations.

There are many different types of puppets. They are made using a variety of materials.

Class activity

1. Discuss different types of puppets you have seen and perhaps used.

   Discuss the characteristics of different puppets.

   Use this framework to aid your discussion.

Type of puppet:	glove, stick, string, marionette
Character:	animal, person
Size:	small, large
Materials used:	wood, polystyrene, papier-mâché
Colours/Decorations:	bright, pastel
Costume:	colourful, national, appropriate for character
Personality:	friendly, angry, happy, gentle
Voice:	loud, soft, harsh
Actions:	flamboyant, rigid

Activity

2. Choose a puppet you would like to describe. Think about what this puppet looks like and the things it might do. Draw and name your puppet.

   Use the semantic web on the next page to collect information about this puppet.

   Prepare a three-minute talk describing the puppet and present it to the class.

   Include all the relevant information from your semantic web.

Semantic web

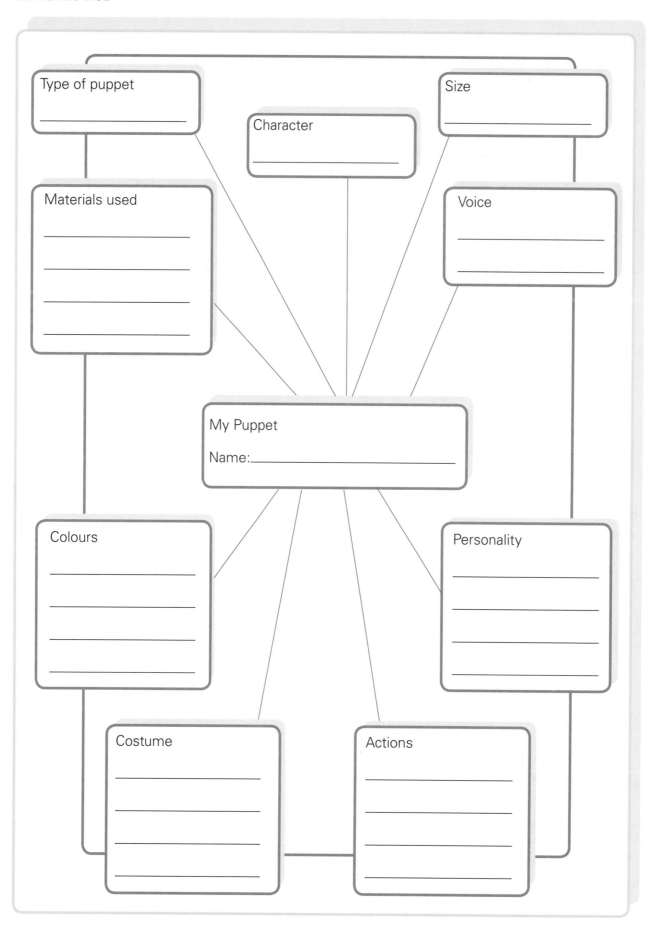

Type of puppet
_____

Character
_____

Size
_____

Materials used
_____
_____
_____
_____

Voice
_____
_____

My Puppet

Name:_____

Colours
_____
_____
_____
_____

Personality
_____
_____
_____

Costume
_____
_____
_____

Actions
_____
_____
_____

> **This procedure has:**
>
> **A goal:** This is at the beginning and tells us what is to be done.
>
> **Requirements:** These are items needed to complete a task.
>
> **Steps:** This is a list, in order, of what you must do.
>
> **Test:** Was the task completed successfully?

Read the procedure for making a wooden spoon puppet. Answer the following questions about the structure of this procedure.

Goal

1. What is the procedure about? _____

_____

Requirements

2. What do you need to complete this task?

_____   _____

_____   _____

_____   _____

_____

Steps

3. The order of the steps in a procedure can be very important. Colour the instructions you would do **first**.

(a)	Sew two lines of stitches.	OR	Pull the thread together.
(b)	Add decorations.	OR	Paint the spoon.
(c)	Glue the fabric around spoon.	OR	Draw eyes, nose and mouth.
(d)	Cut the fabric.	OR	Knot the threads together.
(e)	Glue ribbon around gathers.	OR	Paint the nose, eyes and mouth.

Test

4. How would you know if you have followed the procedure correctly?

_____

_____

_____

Reading for information

True or false? Colour the correct answer.

1. You need to paint all of the spoon the colour of skin. ⭕ **true** ⭕ **false**

2. The puppet can be decorated with scraps of ribbon
    and wool. ⭕ **true** ⭕ **false**

3. You must wait until the paint is dry before adding
    the face. ⭕ **true** ⭕ **false**

4. The gathering at the top of the spoon will be clearly visible. ⭕ **true** ⭕ **false**

5. This puppet would be able to move its arms. ⭕ **true** ⭕ **false**

6. The fabric is glued to the wooden spoon. ⭕ **true** ⭕ **false**

Reading for understanding

1. Do you think this puppet would be suitable for a young child to use? _____

    Why? _____

    _____

    _____

2. Would you need to use a sewing machine to make this puppet? _____

3. How could you show the personality of your puppet? _____

    _____

    _____

    _____

4. How could you make adult and child puppets recognisably different? _____

    _____

    _____

    _____

5. Why would you need:

    (a) a ruler? _____

    _____

    (b) strong glue? _____

    _____

Applying your knowledge

Labels are useful to illustrate procedures.

Draw a wooden spoon puppet below, adding appropriate labels joined by lines to the relevant parts of the puppet.

For example: painted face

gathered stitches

Give your puppet a name.

Word meanings

1. Are the given meanings of these words true or false? Use your dictionary.

    (a) fabric – cloth .... ◯ **true** ◯ **false**

    (b) scrap – to move across a surface .... ◯ **true** ◯ **false**

    (c) additional – added .... ◯ **true** ◯ **false**

    (d) decorate – to improve or beautify............................. ◯ **true** ◯ **false**

    (e) thread – an intention to inflict harm....................... ◯ **true** ◯ **false**

Acrostic

2. (a) Use each letter of the word 'puppet' as the first letter of a word to describe a puppet that appeals to you. Draw your puppet.

    P_____

    U_____

    P_____

    P_____

    E_____

    T_____

    (b) Which is your longest word?

    (c) How many letters does it have?

    (d) Write your three words starting with the letter p.

    (e) Which of these **p** words would you find first in your dictionary?

    (f) Write these **p** words in alphabetical order.

purse	power	pool	present	puddle	poodle

    _____

    _____

Homographs

Homographs are words that are spelt the same but have different meanings.

3.　Use your dictionary to find two different meanings for these words.

(a)　arms

(b)　hand

(c)　watch

Word puzzle

4.　Each box contains a group of three letters from a nine-letter word.

Use these groups to answer the clues below.

The leftover groups will make another nine-letter word.

sno	ing	hib	ina
suf	row	ens	ent
amp	bal	den	ide
mic	foc	ell	ive
gar	exc	ler	ian
exp	wsl	ate	ave

Clues:

1.　A classical dancer b_____

2.　an avalanche s_____

3.　a modern appliance for cooking

　　m_____

4.　a frog or a salamander a_____

5.　working in the garden, growing flowers

　　g_____

6.　fantastic, superb e_____

7.　deprive of air, strangle s_____

The leftover groups make _____

Word snake

5.　(a)　Cross out all the **d s k u** letters in this word snake to find a special type of puppet.

d k m u k a r u d k i s d o u n e s s d t s t e d

_____

(b)　Write a sentence about this particular puppet. _____

_____

Suffixes

Study these rules for adding the suffix **ly**.

Rule 1

There are many rules for adding a suffix, but it is usually just added to the word.

For example: love – love**ly**

                        sudden – sudden**ly**

Rule 2

To add **ly** to words ending in **le** after **a consonant**, change the **e** to **y**.

For example: simple – simp**ly**

                        horrible – horrib**ly**

If **le** follows **a vowel**, just add **ly** to the word. (Rule 1)

For example: sole – sole**ly**

Note: An exception is whole – wholly

1. Use Rules 1 and 2 to add the suffix **ly** to these words.

    (a) noticeable   _____   (b) probable   _____

    (c) pale   _____   (d) comfortable   _____

    (e) vile   _____   (f) juvenile   _____

    (g) knowledgeable _____   (h) terrible   _____

2. Choose an adverb ending in **ly** to complete these sentences.

    (a) The drought-stricken farmer looked _____ at the clouds.

    (b) The dog stared _____ as the family left for their holidays.

    (c) The queen waved _____ as she was driven through the crowd.

    (d) He slammed the ball _____ across the tennis court.

    (e) The display home was _____ decorated.

3. Write your own sentences using these words as adverbs.

    (a) strangely _____

    _____

    (b) weekly   _____

    _____

    (c) weakly   _____

    _____

(d) horribly _____

_____

(e) simply _____

_____

(f) terribly _____

_____

> **Rule 3**
>
> To add **ly** to words ending in **y**, when the **y** makes an **e** sound, the **e** is changed to **i** before adding **ly**.
>
> For example: hungry – hungr**ily**

4. Use the above rule to add **ly** to the highlighted words.

(a) He waved his fist **angry** as the car sped away.

(b) The players left the field **weary**.

(c) The injured worker staggered **clumsy** along the footpath.

(d) They worked **busy** to complete their project.

(e) The crowd cheered **noisy** as the band came onto the stage.

(f) Our dog barked **happy** when we arrived home.

(g) The animal drank the water **thirsty**.

5. Add **ly** to these words.

Remember: Only change the **y** to **i** when the **y** makes an **e** sound.

(a) hungry _____   (b) funny _____

(c) shy _____   (d) speedy _____

(e) happy _____   (f) sly _____

(g) dry _____   (h) silly _____

Adverbs

Adverbs are words which can add meaning to verbs.

They can tell **where**, **when** or **how** something happens.

For example:

Adverbs of place (where)   –   outside, away, nowhere, abroad, near

Adverbs of time (when)   –   yesterday, late, already, now, early

Adverbs of manner (how)   –   clearly, correctly, accurately, skillfully

1. Underline the verb, then circle the adverb in each sentence.

    (a) He walked cautiously around the corner. (manner)

    (b) The plane just landed at the airport. (time)

    (c) They play football outdoors. (place)

    (d) There are flowers everywhere. (place)

    (e) Mary studies abroad. (place)

    (f) The teacher explained the work clearly. (manner)

    (g) The driver stopped suddenly. (manner)

    (h) He fought courageously. (manner)

2. Underline the adverb in each sentence. Rewrite the sentence beginning with the adverb.

    The first one has been done for you.

    (a) The boys <u>often</u> missed the bus.

    > Often, the boys missed the bus.

    (b) He desperately clung to the sinking boat.

    (c) The dancer gracefully leapt across the stage.

    (d) The cow grazed contentedly in the lush, green field.

    (e) The soldiers fought valiantly against the enemy.

    (f) The dog faithfully followed his master.

3. Write sentences using these adverbs of **place** (where).

> upstairs   nowhere   here

(a) _____

_____

_____

(b) _____

_____

_____

(c) _____

_____

_____

4. Write sentences using these adverbs of **time** (when).

> early   yet   today

(a) _____

_____

_____

(b) _____

_____

_____

(c) _____

_____

_____

5. Write sentences using these adverbs of **manner** (how).

> sarcastically   courteously   realistically

(a) _____

_____

(b) _____

_____

(c) _____

_____

Adjectives to adverbs

6. Change the following words (adjectives) to adverbs by adding suffixes. You may need to revise the spelling rules on page 102.

For example: peaceful – peacefully

Note: Adjectives are words describing nouns.

(a) beautiful _____   (b) absolute _____

(c) extreme _____   (d) temporary _____

(e) occasional _____   (f) accurate _____

Read the procedure *Wooden spoon puppet* again and answer the following questions.

Text organisation

1. Test – How would you know if the procedure was followed successfully?

   _____

   _____

2. Is the *sequence* of the steps in this procedure relevant? _____

   Why/Why not? _____

   _____

3. What skills would a person need to successfully complete this procedure?

   _____

   _____

Language features

4. Why do statements in procedures need to be clear and concise?

   _____

   _____

5. What tense is used in this procedure? _____

Activities

Clear concise language

1. Rewrite each of these using clear, concise language, command verbs and very few words. For example:

   You will need to take two pieces of material and place them together, edge to edge, with right sides facing. Stitch along the edge using a sewing machine so that the pieces are joined.

   > Sew fabric together.

   (a) If you want to have a balloon to play with you will need to blow air into it. It helps if you stretch the balloon first by pulling it, then place your lips on the opening and blow air inside it until it is inflated. Then you can tie it up.

   (b) After you have taken the piece of string and wrapped it around a parcel that you want to post to a friend, it is important that you get some scissors and use them to cut the ends off the string.

Choose one topic from the box and use the framework to write a procedure. You may need to research appropriate information on the Internet, in the library or seek advice from another person.

Making toffee   *Building a sandcastle*

Washing a dog   *Growing strawberries*

TITLE: _____

GOAL: _____

_____

REQUIREMENTS:

_____

_____

_____

_____

STEPS: _____

_____

_____

_____

_____

_____

_____

_____

_____

_____

TEST: (How will you know if the procedure was completed successfully?)

_____

_____

_____

Use the checklist below to edit and proofread your work.

You will self-edit for:

Spelling   Punctuation

Grammar   Sentence structure

You will use a peer editor to check for:

Clear instructions and sense

Checklist

Title of the procedure: _____

1. Does your procedure make sense to you? .... ○ **yes** ○ **no**

2. Did you include a goal? .... ○ **yes** ○ **no**

3. Did you list the things you need? .... ○ **yes** ○ **no**

4. Are the steps in logical, effective order? .... ○ **yes** ○ **no**

5. Are there unnecessary bits of information? .... ○ **yes** ○ **no**

6. Did you add a test to check the procedure works? .... ○ **yes** ○ **no**

7. Have you corrected any spelling errors? .... ○ **yes** ○ **no**

    (a)   Did you check that your words look right? .... ○ **yes** ○ **no**

    (b)   Did you use a dictionary? .... ○ **yes** ○ **no**

    (c)   Did you ask someone? .... ○ **yes** ○ **no**

8. Have you used command verbs? .... ○ **yes** ○ **no**

9. Do all your statements have capital letters and full stops? .... ○ **yes** ○ **no**

10. Is your procedure written in the present tense? .... ○ **yes** ○ **no**

11. Ask a partner to read your procedure.
    Did he or she find it easy to understand? .... ○ **yes** ○ **no**

---

1. Choose a topic from the box, then plan and write a procedure on a separate sheet of paper.

> • **making pizza**   • **taking a photo**   • **maintaining a bicycle**
>
> • **making a bed**   • **using a DVD player**   • **washing dishes**

2. Complete these statements.

   (a) Procedures are usually written in the

   _____ tense.

   (b) Procedures usually use

   _____ verbs.

   (c) It is important to follow the steps in sequence because _____

   _____

   _____

3. Homographs look the same, their meanings are _____.

4. Write two different meanings for these words.

   (a) watch

   (b) duck

   (c) chip

5. | ing | ed | er | ful | est | ly |

   These are called _____ and they are attached to the _____
   of words.

6. Add the suffix **ly** to these words.

   (a) miserable

   (b) terrible

   (c) futile

   (d) pale

   (e) probable

   (f) comfortable

7. Add **ly** to these words.

    (a) shy _____   (b) crazy _____

    (c) hungry _____   (d) speedy _____

    (e) noisy _____   (f) sly _____

8. Adverbs usually add meaning to _____.

9. Underline the verbs, then circle the adverbs.

    > (a) He stared anxiously at his maths test.

    > (b) Enthusiastically, the hikers approached the walking trail.

    > (c) Mr Jones warily watched the ferocious animal.

    > (d) The bus stopped abruptly.

    > (e) Yesterday, she walked to school.

    > (f) The children ran upstairs.

10. Write **place**, **time** or **manner** to classify the highlighted adverbs.

    (a) Do your homework **now**.

    (b) Watch **carefully** so that you will learn to do this by yourself.

    (c) Put your swimsuit and towel **away**.

    (d) She arrived at school **early**.

    (e) Leave your boots **outside**.

    (f) The horses reached the river and drank **thirstily**.

    (g) The class worked **hard**.

11. Change these words (adjectives) to **adverbs** by adding **ly**.

    (a) courteous _____   (b) busy _____

    (c) beautiful _____   (d) funny _____

    (e) wonderful _____   (f) timid _____

Just not cricket

A recount is a retelling of past events in time order.
Recounts can be personal, factual or imaginative.

Read the **recount**.

Just not cricket

Ever since I was a little boy I've wanted to play cricket professionally. I love the game.

I admire those famous players bowling down the pitch, their arms swinging in a perfect arc, the batter waiting in anticipation. I remember when I was about 10, my mother took me to the Lord's Cricket Ground to tour the grounds and the trophy rooms. I walked out onto the cricket pitch and imagined the spectators applauding me as I hit a century.

Now that dream seems to be slipping away. I have been playing on Fridays at school, as well as Saturdays with the local team. Last year I was in the A-team. This year I have been demoted to the B-team. How embarrassing! I don't know what has happened to me, but I just don't seem to have any luck. I drop all the catches when I am in the field and have not made a single run in the last ten matches I've played—getting out for a duck each time. My dad tries hard to help me, giving me extra practice after school each day; sometimes we even go and practise at 6 o'clock in the morning. It has become so bad that I even overheard the coach suggesting to the team manager that I should get my eyes tested.

I must admit that I am totally perplexed and am losing confidence in myself. Perhaps golf or football would be a better option for me.

The English workbook

Class activity

> The writer should get things in perspective or **get real**. It's only sport!

Discuss this statement.

Do you agree or disagree? _____

How many pupils in your class agree? _____ disagree? _____

Brainstorm arguments to support both points of view and write them on the board.

After having listened to both sides of this argument, have you changed your opinion? _____

Prepare a one-minute talk to support your point of view and try to persuade someone in the class to change his or her opinion.

Partner activity

Working with a partner, discuss what you think might happen next and why you think this.

> Will the writer continue to play cricket?
>
> Will he improve?
>
> What could help this happen?
>
> Will participating in a different sport have the same or a different result?

There is of course no right or wrong answer, but it is important that you give logical reasons to support your opinions.

Structure of a recount

Structure	
This recount has:	
A title:	**What** the recount is about
A setting:	**Who** the recount is about
	Where the events happened
	When the events happened
	Why the events happened
The events:	**What** happened
	Events are told in the order in which they happened.
	Each major event is written in a new paragraph.
An ending/Comment:	The ending and what the writer **thinks** about the events.

Read the recount about cricket again. Answer these questions.

TITLE

What is the recount about? _____

SETTING

(a) Who is the recount about?

_____

(b) Where does he play?

_____

(c) When does he play cricket?

_____

_____

(d) Why is he unhappy?

_____

_____

EVENTS

1. When did the boy first become interested in cricket? _____

_____

2. Where did his mother take him? _____

_____

3. What team did he play with last year? _____

4. What team is he in now? _____

5. How well has he been playing? _____

6. How did his dad try to help? _____

_____

7. What did the coach want him to do? _____

_____

ENDING OR COMMENT

What does the boy think about playing cricket now? _____

_____

Reading for information

True or false?

Colour the correct answer.

1. The coach was not concerned about the writer's cricket performance.   ○ **true** ○ **false**

2. The boy has only hit a few runs in his last 10 matches.   ○ **true** ○ **false**

3. His dad practises with him early in the morning.   ○ **true** ○ **false**

4. He thinks that he might do better at tennis or basketball.   ○ **true** ○ **false**

5. Tourists at the Lord's Cricket Ground are sometimes allowed onto the cricket pitch.   ○ **true** ○ **false**

Reading for understanding

Use complete sentences to explain your answers to these questions.

1. Do you think that the boy's dad is interested in cricket?

   ○ **yes** ○ **no**

   Why do you think this?

   _____

   _____

   _____

   _____

   _____

2. Do you think the boy has been really trying to do well at cricket?

   ○ **yes** ○ **no**

   Explain why you think this.

   _____

   _____

   _____

   _____

3. (a) Cricket is meant to be 'just' a game. Why do you think the author chose the title?

   _____

   _____

   _____

   _____

   (b) Do you think it is an appropriate title?

   ○ **yes** ○ **no**

4. The boy's problems could be bad luck or could be the result of other factors. What do you think could be the problem(s)? Give reasons for your opinion.

   _____

   _____

   _____

   _____

Applying your knowledge

1. The boy in the recount had a dream. His dream was to be a very successful cricketer.

    What are four things you could suggest he does to try to achieve this goal?

2. Cricket, like most games, has formal rules to ensure that both teams have an equal chance of winning.

    Research the rules to answer these questions.

    (a) How many players in each team?

    (b) How many batsmen are allowed on the field?

    (c) What is one rule about the bowler? _____

    _____

    _____

    (d) What does the batsman have to do to score six runs? _____

    _____

    (e) What does LBW mean? _____

    (f) How many balls are bowled in an over?

    (g) Where are these famous cricket grounds:

        (i) Lords?   _____ (ii) MCG?   _____

        (iii) Wanderers? _____ (iv) Queens Park? _____

    (h) What is a 'duck' in cricket? _____

    _____

    _____

Dictionary meanings

1. Find the meanings of these words.

(a) perplex

(b) option

(c) demote

(d) arc

(e) anticipation

(f) spectator

Partner activity

Shades of meaning

The three words in each group are related in meaning but the differences between them are called 'shades of meaning'.

Take turns with your partner to explain how the three words differ in meaning. You may need to consult a dictionary.

2.
(a) house
   cottage
   mansion

(b) sleep
   rest
   nap

(c) mob
   group
   congregation

(d) talk
   tell
   instruct

(e) ask
   beg
   demand

(f) river
   creek
   canal

3. Choose the 'best' (most descriptive) word.

(a) The girl who (walked, dawdled) to school was late.

(b) Jill (stared, looked) at the strange looking animal.

(c) The strong wind (slammed, blew) the door shut with a loud bang.

(d) In a fit of temper, the tennis player (broke, smashed) his racquet.

More interesting words

4. Compile a list of alternative, more descriptive words or phrases for the overused words on the chart below.

said	went	then
squealed	sailed	eventually

got	asked	saw
contracted	queried	witnessed

Confusing words

There are many words which are often confused because they sound the same or look similar.

For example: quiet   quite

Choose the correct words.

> Quiet is the opposite of loud.
>
> Quite means almost, somewhat or rather.

1. (a) I think her dress is _____ attractive.

    (b) The library is a _____ place.

    (c) Please be _____.

    (d) The toddler couldn't _____ reach the table.

> Waste means to use badly.
>
> Waist is the middle part of the body.

2. (a) Water is precious, please don't

    _____ it.

    (b) She tied the belt tightly around her

    _____.

    (c) His _____ measured 77 cm.

    (d) He threw his messy work into the

    _____ paper bin.

> Stationery is material for writing on (paper, envelopes).
>
> Stationary means not moving.

3. (a) The train was _____.

    (b) At the traffic lights, many impatient drivers were sitting in their

    _____ cars.

    (c) I need some _____ for school.

    (d) You can buy _____ at the newsagent.

> Pray is to worship or ask for something.
>
> Prey is something that is being hunted.

4. (a) The eagle swooped and seized its

    _____.

    (b) I _____ that you will recover soon.

    (c) The cat was stalking its _____.

    (d) The priest will _____ in church on Sunday.

Homophones

Homophones are words that sound the same but have different meanings.

For example: meat   meet

Did you notice that some of the **confusing words** you looked at are **homophones** (pray, prey) and some are slightly different in sound (quiet, quite)?

Short and long vowels

Spelling rule

The letter **e** at the end of a word changes a short vowel sound to a long vowel sound.

Read these words and notice how this rule works.

rat	rate
pet	Pete
rid	ride
hop	hope
cub	cube

5. (a) Add **e** to these short vowel words to make words with long vowel sounds.

pan [ ]   not [ ]   us [ ]

rod [ ]   slid [ ]   fad [ ]

(b) Use the long vowel words you made in sentences.

- _____
- _____
- _____
- _____
- _____
- _____

Spelling rule

When adding a suffix to a word, two consonants keep the vowel short.

(A suffix is a group of letters added to the end of a word; e.g. **ing**, **y**, **ed**.)

6. Read these words. They all have short vowels and they all have two consonants.

slipping	kicked	drinking	skipping

Underline the short vowels in the base words and circle the double consonants.

Notice that with the words **slip** and **skip** which have only one consonant at the end, it was necessary to double that consonant.

7. Add **ing** to these words.

Ask yourself if the vowel is long or short.

(a) swim   (b) sink   (c) shop   (d) hand

_____   _____   _____   _____

hope ride slide shape

These words have long vowel sounds. There is a rule for adding a suffix to words with long vowel sounds ending with **e**.

Spelling rule

When adding a suffix starting with a vowel to a word ending with a silent **e**, drop the **e** because the suffix acts in the same way and keeps the vowel long.

hope	hoping
ride	riding
slide	sliding
shape	shaping

A simple way of remembering this rule is:

'**e** goes away when **ing** comes to stay'.

8. Add **ing** or **ed** to these words.

(a) shave   _____   (b) slope   _____

(c) bite   _____   (d) use   _____

(e) shape   _____   (f) face   _____

Pronouns

A pronoun is a word substituted for a noun.

For example: **he** for **Bill**, **they** for Bill and Jake

1. (a) Rewrite this passage, replacing the highlighted words with pronouns.

> Since Peter was a little boy, **Peter** has wanted to play cricket professionally. **Peter** loves the game. **Peter** admires many famous players. **Peter's** dad tries to help **Peter** by giving **Peter** extra practice but **Peter's** game has not improved. Peter thinks that **Peter** might try golf or football because **golf or football** could suit **Peter** better.

_____

(b) All the pronouns you used, except one, are called **personal pronouns** because they refer to people.

What is the exception? _____

Personal pronouns can be singular or plural.

2. Read these personal pronouns and indicate if they are singular **s** (one person) or plural **p** (more than one person).

(a) I	(b) us	(c) them
(d) me	(e) ours	(f) you
(g) we	(h) mine	(i) her
(j) he	(k) yours	(l) she
(m) they	(n) his	(o) myself

Personal pronouns take different forms depending on whether they are referring to:

The person doing the talking (First Person); e.g. **I**.

The person being spoken to (Second Person); e.g. **you**.

The person being spoken about (Third Person); e.g. **he**.

3. (a) Write these personal pronouns in the appropriate boxes.

> you   they   she   I   he   we

First person	Second person	Third person

(b) Add these pronouns to the above lists.

> me   us   yours   his   mine   ours   hers   theirs   it

Nouns

There are four types of nouns.

1. **Common nouns** are words that name a general rather than a particular thing; e.g. book, mountain, ship.

2. **Proper nouns** are words that name particular people, places and things. They need capital letters; e.g. Margaret, London, Pacific Ocean.

3. **Abstract nouns** are words that name feelings, states and actions; things that we cannot see; e.g. thirst, courage, loyalty, speed.

4. **Collective nouns** are words that name groups of people or things; e.g. audience, team, bunch, flock.

    Some collective nouns are quite common and others are unusual and interesting.

4. What are these collective nouns used for? You will need to research some of your answers.

(a) a school of _____

(b) a gaggle of _____

(c) a raft of _____

(d) a convocation of _____

(e) a fleet of _____

(f) a coven of _____

(g) a stand of _____

(h) a parliament of _____

(i) a galaxy of _____

(j) a dray of _____

Sequencing

Writing the events of a recount in the order in which they happen is important. We must also ensure that no important events are omitted.

For example: for a recount about cleaning teeth we would probably need to include:

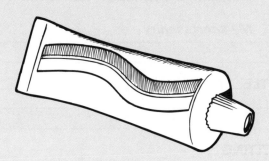

- going to the bathroom
- finding toothbrush and toothpaste
- opening the tube of toothpaste
- placing toothpaste on the brush
- cleaning teeth
- rinsing mouth
- drying mouth

1. (a) Think about the things you do and the order in which you do them when you are going to school in the morning. List at least eight events involved.

    - _____
    - _____
    - _____
    - _____
    - _____
    - _____
    - _____
    - _____

    (b) Is the order of the events you listed important? _____

    (c) What could happen if you did things in a different sequence?

    _____
    _____
    _____

    (d) Did you miss out any events? _____

    (e) How could this affect your recount?

    _____
    _____
    _____

Choose a topic from the box, then plan and write a recount on a separate sheet of paper.

- *Playing tennis/hockey/basketball/football/golf – or a sport of your choice.*

- *Watching the football grand final*

- *Watching the tennis at Wimbledon*

- *My sports injury*

TITLE _____

SETTING

Who

Where

When

Why

EVENTS

1. _____
   _____

2. _____
   _____

3. _____
   _____

4. _____
   _____

ENDING OR COMMENT

_____

_____

_____

After you have written your recount in full, edit and proofread your work using the checklist below.

You will self-edit for:

Spelling   Punctuation

Grammar   Sentence structure

You will use a peer editor to check for:

Sense and sequence

Checklist

Title: _____

Setting

1. Does your recount include:

    • specific characters? (who) .... ○ **yes** ○ **no**

    • location or setting? (where) .... ○ **yes** ○ **no**

    • time when events took place? (when) .... ○ **yes** ○ **no**

    • why these events occurred? (why) .... ○ **yes** ○ **no**

Events

2. Were your events listed in correct order? .... ○ **yes** ○ **no**

Conclusion

3. Did your recount finish with a concluding comment or statement? .... ○ **yes** ○ **no**

Spelling

4. • Have you corrected any spelling errors? .... ○ **yes** ○ **no**

    • Have you used capital letters and full stops? .... ○ **yes** ○ **no**

Grammar

5. • Did you include action verbs? .... ○ **yes** ○ **no**

    • Did you use conjunctions? .... ○ **yes** ○ **no**

    • Did you use the past tense? .... ○ **yes** ○ **no**

6. Ask a partner to read your recount.

    • Was your partner able to follow the sequence? .... ○ **yes** ○ **no**

    • Did it make sense? .... ○ **yes** ○ **no**

1. Choose a topic from the box and plan and write a recount in full on a separate sheet of paper. Use the editing and proofreading sheet as a guide to check your work.

    - *The cricket windup*   - *The party*
    - *After the finals*   - *The celebration*
    - *We won after all*

2. Complete the following statements.

    Text: What is a recount?

    _____

    _____

    _____

    _____._____

    _____

3. Structure of a recount: A recount has

    - a _____

    - a setting which tells who

      _____, _____

      and _____.

    - events

    - an _____

4. Choose the correct word to complete the sentence.

    quiet   quite   waste   waist   prey   pray   stationery   stationary

    (a) You can purchase ⌷_____⌷ at the local newsagent.

    (b) The ⌷_____⌷ treatment plant must comply with strict environmental guidelines.

    (c) The paratrooper had to tie the parachute securely around his ⌷_____⌷.

    (d) The lioness was skilled at stalking her ⌷_____⌷.

    (e) The Queen's guard at Buckingham Palace was standing ⌷_____⌷ at his post.

    (f) We ⌷_____⌷ that war will be averted.

    (g) The pupils did not ⌷_____⌷ finish their exam essay.

    (h) The rowdy airline passenger was asked to be ⌷_____⌷.

5. When adding a suffix to a word, two consonants keep the vowel _____

6. Add **er**, **ed**, or **ing** to these words.

(a) swim [   ]   (b) shop [   ]

(c) slide [   ]   (d) hope [   ]

(e) ride [   ]   (f) hand [   ]

(g) shave [   ]   (h) use [   ]

(i) face [   ]   (j) slope [   ]

A pronoun is a word substituted for a noun. It can be **singular** or **plural**.

7. (a) Read the passage below. Highlight the 13 pronouns in the passage.

> Mandy enjoys the basketball she plays every weekend. Some friends are also members of the basketball association and they all play at Matthews Basketball Stadium. Mandy lost a good towel and thought that Jill might have it.
>
> 'I think that towel is mine not yours', she said, but it wasn't hers.
>
> 'Mum won't be happy with me', she moaned. 'I'll be in trouble for losing it.'

(b) Which is the only plural pronoun in the passage?   _____

(c) Which pronoun is used three times?   _____

(d) There is only one second person (the person spoken to) pronoun used. What is it?

_____

8. Complete these collective nouns.

(a) a school of [   ]   (b) a stand of [   ]

(c) a raft of [   ]   (d) a parliament of [   ]

(e) a [   ] of stars   (f) a bunch of [   ]

(g) a [   ] of birds   (h) a [   ] of cattle

(i) a [   ] of ships   (j) a [   ] of wolves

Fair go for skateboarders

ANALYSIS

Expositions analyse, interpret and evaluate the environment around us. Their purpose is to persuade by presenting one side of an argument.

Read the **exposition**.

Fair go for skateboarders

I'm a skateboarder who felt very sad and angry when I read the letter written by Ken Smith. It is not right that he should be frightened, but skateboarders need a safe place to enjoy their sport.

Footballers are provided with pitches, basketballers have stadiums and even surfers have the beach, but skateboarders have nowhere. If we skate on the road, we get into trouble. Where else is there?

Skateboarding is inexpensive, it's a healthy, outdoor activity which is physically demanding and challenging. It doesn't pollute or harm the environment, but it is not supported by anyone.

The answer is obvious. Instead of complaining about us, what about providing us with a skateboarding venue? Our parents would know exactly where we are and what we are doing. It is actually a spectacular sport to watch. Mr. Smith might even enjoy it and, what's more, it's free.

So instead of banning this activity, what about supporting us by asking the council to provide appropriate facilities that should keep everyone happy?

Sam Simpson

Partner activity

1. (a) Working with a partner, discuss and compile a list of good things about skateboarding.

Include those from the exposition and add some of your own.

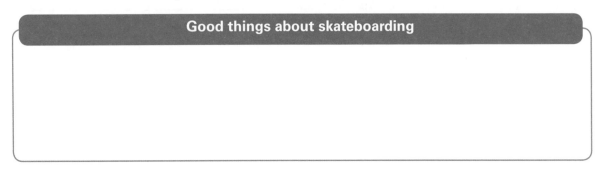

Good things about skateboarding

(b) Compare your list with another group's and highlight any that are in both groups' lists.

(c) What do you think is the best thing about skateboarding?

Class activity

One of the issues in this exposition concerns a suitable venue.

Compile a list of activities your class members enjoy and add the venue or venues where these activities take place.

For example:

Activity	Venues
horse riding	woods, beach, pony club

Discuss whether all of these activities are provided with adequate venues and if not, what needs to be done about it.

Structure of an exposition

Structure

An exposition uses persuasive language to present a particular point of view.

An exposition can have:

A title:	Tells what the exposition is about.
An overview:	Briefly tells what the writer thinks about the subject.
Reasons:	Arguments to persuade people.
Conclusion:	Final comment and summing up.

Read *Fair go for skateboarders* again.

Answer these questions.

Title: What is the exposition about? _____

_____

_____

Overview: What does the writer want? _____

_____

_____

Reasons: 1. Why does the writer list venues provided for other activities?

_____

_____

_____

2. What are three positive attributes of skateboarding?

• _____

• _____

• _____

3. How would a skateboarding venue be good for parents?

_____

_____

_____

4. How could a skateboarding venue be of value to the community?

_____

_____

_____

Conclusion: What does the writer want people to do? _____

_____

_____

Reading for information

True or false?

Highlight the correct answer.

(a) The writer is very sad and cross because Ken Smith doesn't
understand that skateboarders have nowhere else to ride. ....○ **true** ○ **false**

(b) The writer wants skateboarders to be allowed to skate on the road. ....○ **true** ○ **false**

(c) The writer thinks that scaring older people is good fun. ....○ **true** ○ **false**

(d) Skateboarding can be fun to watch. ....○ **true** ○ **false**

(e) If skateboarders had a suitable venue their parents would know where
they were and they would be safer. ....○ **true** ○ **false**

Reading for understanding

(a) How do you think Ken Smith might feel
after reading this exposition? Do you think
he will still want skateboarding banned?

_____

Explain your reasons.

_____

_____

_____

_____

_____

(b) What do you think the local council **will**
do?

_____

_____

_____

_____

_____

(c) What do you think the local council **should**
do?

_____

_____

_____

_____

_____

_____

(d) Which argument (reason) given by the
skateboarder do you think is the most
convincing?

_____

_____

_____

_____

_____

_____

Applying your knowledge

(a) How do you think your grandparents would feel about skateboarding in shopping centres?

_____
_____
_____

(b) What are some of the possible dangers associated with skateboarding?

_____
_____
_____
_____

(c) How could people skateboarding in parks and on footpaths be more considerate of others?

_____
_____
_____

(d) Ken Smith complained that the skateboarders laughed when he was frightened by them. Do you think they thought that frightening older people was funny or could there be a different explanation? Give reasons for your answer.

_____
_____
_____
_____
_____

(e) Who do you think is more persuasive, Ken Smith or Sam Simpson? _____
Explain why you think this.

_____
_____
_____
_____

1. (a) Write an acrostic poem. Try to use appropriate and interesting words. Write three words for each letter and highlight the best ones, then write them on the board below.

S

K

A

T

E

B

O

A

R

D

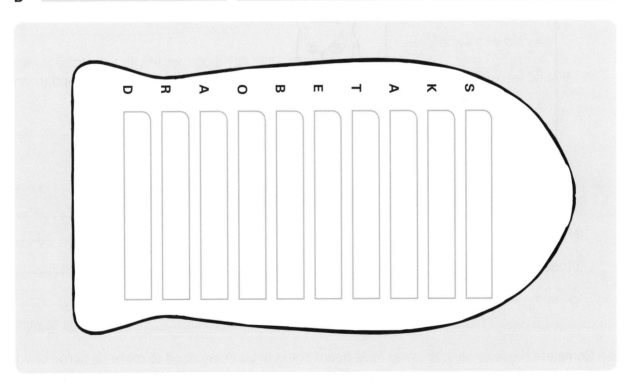

(b) Which letter did you find most difficult to find words for?

(c) How many of the words you chose for your acrostic were in the text of *Fair go for skateboarders*?

Crack the code

A	B	C	D	E	F	G	H	I	J	K	L	M	N	O	P	Q	R	S	T	U	V	W	X	Y	Z
		A					F											Q							

2. (a) The code above has been started for you. Find the pattern and complete the missing letters.

    (b) Use the code to write this message.

    C o d e s   a r e   f u n.

Similes

    Am__ __ __   __ __ __   __ __ __

A simile points out the likeness between two generally unlike things.

3. Use the same code to solve these similes.

    (a) YQ OSGAI YQ Y UGLI   _____

    (b) YQ AMJB YQ GAC   _____

    (c) YQ AJCYP YQ KSB   _____

4. (a) Make up a code and use it to write one of the similes below. You may choose to use letters or numerals.

A	B	C	D	E	F	G	H	I	J	K	L	M	N	O	P	Q	R	S	T	U	V	W	X	Y	Z

> As slow as a snail
>
> As busy as a bee
>
> As wise as an owl
>
> As sick as a dog

Coded simile _____

(b) Ask a partner to use your code to work out which simile you chose and to write it below.

_____

5. Make up a simile of your own to describe each of these.

    (a) butter   _____

    (b) sugar   _____

    (c) summer   _____

6. Complete these similes. You may have heard some or you may need to make up some of your own.

    (a) as smooth as   [   ]

    (b) as fast as   [   ]

    (c) as skinny as   [   ]

7. Use the nine letters in each puzzle to solve the clue.

(a)

w	s	r
p	n	e
a	p	e

something we read daily

n_____

(b)

u	t	h
g	a	o
r	a	p

a signature

a_____

(c)

a	l	b
u	m	c
a	n	e

an emergency vehicle

a_____

(d)

a	e	i
l	p	n
e	p	p

a fruit

p_____

(e)

t	a	p
g	s	h
t	i	e

something we eat

s_____

(f)

a	n	u
c	h	r
i	r	e

a fierce storm

h_____

Nine letter words

8. Use these groups of three letters to solve the clues. The leftover words will make another nine-letter word.

sew	nes	les	gus	ara	akf
uti	pet	bre	lic	bal	ger
sen	rol	day	bea	eum	ate
dup	ang	ful	hou	ork	tri
Wed	ler	ast	pas	asp	ina

(a) the first meal of the day   b_____

(b) a long green vegetable   a_____

(c) three-sided shapes   t_____

(d) fuel for vehicles   p_____

(e) a classical dancer   b_____

(f) a copy   d_____

(g) job done at home   h_____

(h) middle day of the school week   W_____

(i) a traveller on a bus or train   p_____

(j) The left over letters make   b_____

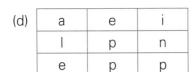

9. Complete the crossword using words from the narrative.

Across
6. Opposite to no-one
7. Mothers and fathers
10. To find fault
11. The same for everyone
12. Sand and sea
13. Response to a question
19. Where we live
20. Make available
21. Easy to see
23. Provided to make activities easier
25. An area
26. Where basketball is played

Down
1. Cheap
2. Place
3. In good health
4. Stopping
5. Exercise
8. Free from danger
9. Testing
14. Things you do
15. Scared
16. Difficulty
17. Correct
18. Written communication
22. Track
24. Cross

'Tricky' bits

Learning to spell words correctly is easier if you can identify the difficult or **tricky bit** of the word and focus your attention on it.

For example:

Skateboarder   The 'tricky bit' for most people is the **a** in board because **or** is a more common spelling than **oar**.

1. (a) Circle the **tricky bits** in these words from the exposition. Try matching the letters to the sounds in the words.

stadium	trouble
physically	environment
answer	venue
watch	know
council	instead

(b) Spend five to ten minutes trying to teach yourself the 10 words. Focus on the **tricky bits**.

(c) Ask someone to test you on the 10 words.

(d) How many words did you spell correctly?   _____

(e) If you made any errors, were they in the 'tricky parts'? _____

Contractions

In English we often leave out letters when two words are joined because it is quicker and easier to say. An apostrophe is used to indicate that letters have been omitted.

For example: I would   I'd

2. Complete this table showing words and contractions.

	contraction	word	word	letter(s) omitted
(a)	she'll		will	wi
(b)	I'd	I		
(c)		will	not	
(d)	they'd			
(e)		were	not	
(f)	don't		not	

3. Write a sentence using the contractions of these words.

(a) it   will

(b) could   not

(c) shall   not

(d) he   would

(e) did   not

(f) will   not

4. Use this table to make contractions using words from across the top and down the side. You may need to change the word order for some. Don't forget the **apostrophes**!

		will	has/have	is/am/are	would
(a)	**I**				
(b)	**you**				
(c)	**he**			he's	
(d)	**she**				
(e)	**it**				
(f)	**we**				
(g)	**they**		they've		
(h)	**not**				

5. Underline the contractions and write the two words on the lines.

(a) I won't be at training tomorrow. _____ _____

(b) Dad said we mustn't be late. _____ _____

(c) I think it'll rain tomorrow. _____ _____

Emotive language

Writers of expositions often use emotive language because they want to persuade people to accept their point of view and they do this by appealing to feelings or emotions.

An exposition has to **appear** clear, logical and have well-reasoned arguments. By using emotive language, writers try to achieve the effect they want, while seeming to be neutral.

Read these two different descriptions of the same event.

> A. The surfer's four-wheel drive spun out of control and destroyed the traffic lights after ploughing across the grass.

> B. The car skidded across the grass and hit the traffic lights.

1. (a) Which driver, A or B, do you think was younger?

   (b) Which accident, A or B, do you think was more likely to have been the driver's fault?

   (c) Do you think the writer wanted you to blame this driver?   ○ **yes** ○ **no**

   (d) How did the writer give you this message? Which words did the writer use to give the impression that this driver was more at fault?

   _____

   _____

2. Use some of these emotive words to write three sentences to make a reader feel angry. Choose any additional words you want to use.

thoughtless	thief	sly	failure	greedy
dangerous	dropout	delinquent	destroyed	wasted
aggressive	fugitive	con man	smashed	damaged

   (a) _____

   _____

   (b) _____

   _____

   (c) _____

   _____

Punctuation

Commas

Commas are used to clarify meaning in different ways.

(a) To separate a list of names, descriptions or actions.

   •   The skateboarder wore bright yellow shorts, a blue top, knee pads, elbow pads and a bike helmet.

(b) To show where someone reading aloud would naturally take a breath.

   •   On his way to the park, the skateboarder tripped and hurt his knee.

(c) To separate the name of a person from the rest of the sentence.

   •   Bill Green, the best athlete at our school, spends lots of time skateboarding.

3.   Add commas where they are needed.

   (a) *Tyrannosaurus rex* the largest dinosaur was carnivorous.

   (b) I had a bad day on Saturday because our football team lost my shorts were ripped I played very badly and it poured with rain.

   (c) My father was late picking me up from training but he couldn't help it because there was a traffic jam.

   (d) As we were walking to school a rainbow appeared in the sky.

   (e) For dinner he ate two hamburgers a big box of chips a large strawberry ice-cream and drank a bottle of chocolate milk.

Using punctuation

4.   Punctuate this passage using a red pen.

> the flinders ranges are spectacular geologists have speculated that they may have
>
> once been comparable in size to the himalayas but they have been worn down to their
>
> present size over eons there are many jagged peaks and deep gorges clay pans and salt
>
> lakes can be found in the north while in other areas permanent underground springs
>
> produce surprising lushness over the last century the region's biodiversity has been
>
> damaged prior to the arrival of europeans the flinders ranges were alive with nocturnal
>
> animals such as bilbies bettongs woylies and mulgaras.

Facts and opinions

Expositions often present opinions as facts. Discerning readers need to be able to recognise this.

For example: Skateboarding is dangerous.

Skateboarding is fun.

These are both opinions, but people who agree with them could sometimes believe them to be facts.

1. Read *Fair go for skateboarders* again and find four **opinions** to add to the list.

   (a) It's a healthy, outdoor activity.

   (b) _____

   (c) _____

   (d) _____

   (e) _____

2. Research four facts about skateboarding to add to the list.

   (a) Skateboards have wheels.

   (b) _____

   (c) _____

   (d) _____

   (e) _____

Introductory statements

The introductory statement briefly tells what the author thinks about the subject. It states his/her point of view.

3. Read this paragraph.

   What is the author's position?

   > Many schools require their pupils to wear school uniforms. This gives pupils a sense of belonging and pride in their school. It avoids competition to wear the latest and most expensive fashion trends.

   The author believes _____

   _____

   _____

4. What do you believe? Write two persuasive arguments for **or** against these statements.

   (a) Skateboarders should wear helmets.

   • _____
   _____

   • _____
   _____

(b) Computer games are educational.

- _____
  _____

- _____
  _____

(c) Teachers need a sense of humour.

- _____
  _____

- _____
  _____

Sequencing arguments

Persuasive writers support their opinions by presenting their strongest arguments first.

5. Highlight which of your two arguments in the previous exercise is the stronger.

6. (a) Write four persuasive arguments for **or** against this statement.

Entrance to museums and zoos should be free.

- [   ]

- [   ]

- [   ]

- [   ]

(b) Which argument do you think was your strongest and most persuasive? _____

(c) Which was your least powerful argument? _____

(d) Did you start with your most powerful argument?   ○ **yes** ○ **no**

Choose one of the topics from What do you believe? on pages 141 to 142. Use this plan to help organise your ideas. Then write your exposition in full on a separate sheet of paper.

TITLE _____

INTRODUCTORY STATEMENT

(What do you believe?) _____

_____

_____

_____

ARGUMENTS

(Thoughts and ideas which support what you believe.) _____

_____

_____

_____

_____

_____

_____

_____

_____

_____

_____

_____

_____

_____

CONCLUSION

(Link your ideas together to form a final comment which summarises your position.)

_____

_____

_____

_____

After you have written your exposition in full, use this checklist to edit and proofread your work.

You will self-edit for:

Spelling   Punctuation

Grammar   Sentence structure

You will use a peer editor to check for:

Sense and persuasion

Checklist

Title of exposition: _____

1. Do you understand the purpose of an exposition? .... ○ **yes** ○ **no**

2. Does your exposition ...

   •   clearly state a problem in the introduction? .... ○ **yes** ○ **no**

   •   provide background information? .... ○ **yes** ○ **no**

   •   list reasons to support your belief or view? .... ○ **yes** ○ **no**

   •   use facts to support argument? .... ○ **yes** ○ **no**
       (diagrams, photographs, facts and figures)

   •   sequence arguments from strongest to weakest? .... ○ **yes** ○ **no**

   •   include a final paragraph which reinforces and
       summarises main points?. .... ○ **yes** ○ **no**

3. Have you used persuasive words? .... ○ **yes** ○ **no**

4. Ask your partner to read your exposition.

   •   Did he or she understand your point of view? .... ○ **yes** ○ **no**

   •   Did it make sense? .... ○ **yes** ○ **no**

   •   Were you able to persuade your partner to agree with your
       point of view? .... ○ **yes** ○ **no**

1. Choose a topic from the box and write an exposition in full on a separate sheet of paper. The exposition may be in the form of an essay or a letter. Use the framework on page 143 to plan your exposition.

> Helmets save lives
>
> Parks are for everyone
>
> Protecting our environment

2. Complete the following.

Exposition are written to _____

_____

_____

Expositions use _____ language.

3. Write an acrostic poem about surfing. You may use words or phrases.

S

U

R

F

I

N

G

4. (a) Circle the **tricky bits** in the following words.

   (i) environment   (ii) council   (iii) physically

(b) Write each word in a sentence.

-
-
-

5. Think of a word from the exposition to complete these sentences.

   (a) We went to the st_____ to watch our team play football.

   (b) He had to tell me the an_____ to the question.

   (c) The boy was in tr_____ for throwing sand.

---

6. (a) What is a simile? _____

   (b) Give an example _____

---

7. Write contractions of these words.

   (a) should have [   ]   (b) will not [   ]

   (c) we are [   ]   (d) they have [   ]

   (e) were not [   ]   (f) they are [   ]

   (g) was not [   ]   (h) do not [   ]

8. Underline the emotive words in each sentence and rewrite it using less emotive language.

   The aggressive man destroyed the happy event by yelling belligerently.

   The timber workers would very soon begin their destruction of the magnificent trees in the beautiful, tranquil forest.

9. Punctuate the following by adding commas.

   (a) The skateboarder jumped twisted turned and landed gracefully.

   (b) On his way home the skateboarder bought an ice-cream.

   (c) Brian the school's best skateboarder won the competition.

   (d) Mr Wells the principal rides a motorbike.

   (e) Fearing the worst the farmer went to inspect his stock.

Daring escape

ANALYSIS

A narrative describes a series of events and circumstances, often involving fictitious characters.

Read the **narrative**.

Daring escape

Once upon a time, in the not-so-distant past, there was a young girl called Ping, who lived with her mother and father on a Chinese junk in Hong Kong Harbour. Ping's father was a fisherman and every day they would sail in and out of the harbour. In the middle of the junk was a canopy under which Ping's mother would cook their daily meals of fish and rice. The sleeping quarters were below deck. Special diving birds called cormorants were chained to bamboo poles at the front of the square-shaped bow and each morning Ping could be found singing and talking to the birds. They were her only friends, but she was not unhappy.

One morning, Ping's father announced they would have to travel further afield to find fish. 'There are too many fishermen here and not enough fish to support all these families, I've heard it is better at Lantau', he told his family.

The following morning, before the sun appeared over the peak, Ping and her parents raised the bamboo sail and left the safety of the harbour. Ping knew these waters could be treacherous. She'd heard many stories of pirates patrolling the waters. The most feared was Madame Cheng. Her husband had been the chief of all pirates, but Madame Cheng took control after his death. Stories of her meanness had travelled far and wide. Late in the afternoon of the second day, a pirate ship appeared. Ping caught sight of it and for a long time watched as it followed them. Ping's father raised the second bamboo sail, hoping to catch the wind to help them escape, but to no avail. The pirate ship was too big and too fast.

Just as the sun was slipping beyond the horizon, the pirate ship pulled alongside the junk. A toothless pirate swung onto the deck and grabbed Ping's father. For a moment, Ping was terrified and then she became angry, very angry.

'You have no right to treat my father like that!', she yelled.

'And what are you going to do about it, girlie?', he retorted.

'Watch me!', Ping yelled back. With a thumping heart, Ping grabbed the rope and swung herself across the deck and onto the pirate ship.

All the pirates laughed at her, but Ping didn't care. 'Where is your chief?' she demanded. 'Well, well, if it isn't a slip of a girl', said the chief. At first Ping was surprised and for a second she forgot to be so angry for the pirate chief was none other than Madame Cheng herself.

'Madame Cheng, I have heard of your greatness in these waters, but I beg you to let my family go. We are poor fishermen and have no treasures that could interest you.'

When it seemed that Ping's attempt to save her family had failed, Madame Cheng said very quietly, 'You are a very plucky girl, you remind me of me. Because of your audacity, I will reward you by letting you go'.

Poor Ping nearly collapsed with relief. Her terrified family was relieved. That night, Ping's mother cooked a special meal to celebrate and acknowledge their brave and clever daughter's role in their miraculous escape.

Class activity

Discuss these questions: What are pirates?

Do you think pirates are real?

Why do you think people become pirates?

Name some famous pirates.

Are there pirates today?

What are the differences between traditional and modern pirates?

Partner activity

1. With a partner, imagine you are Ping and you and your family have been attacked by pirates. List 10 more adjectives which describe how you might feel. Use a dictionary to help.

    frightened   scared

2. Pirates often wore eyepatches.

    Discuss why you think they were necessary.

3. Some well-known pirates like Captain Hook had missing limbs.

    Discuss how this may have occurred.

4. Discuss why:

    (a) pirates hide their treasure

    (b) where they hid it

    (c) why they drew maps to find it.

5. Share your ideas with the class.

Structure of a narrative

A narrative has:

A title:	Indicates what the story is about.
	Gets the attention of the reader.
Orientation:	*Who* Main characters and possibly minor characters
	What Initiating event that starts the story
	Where The setting or location
	When Time the story takes place
Complication:	The problem which involves the main character.
Resolution:	How the problem is solved.
Conclusion:	What happened in the end?

Read the story *Daring escape* and answer the questions.

TITLE:

What do you think of when you read the title *Daring escape*? _____

_____

_____

ORIENTATION:

List the characters in the boxes below.

Main characters	Minor characters

What event starts the story?

Where does the story take place?

When does the story take place?

COMPLICATION:

What is the problem the main character must overcome? _____

_____

_____

RESOLUTION:

How was the problem solved? _____

_____

_____

CONCLUSION:

What happened in the end? _____

_____

_____

Reading for information

True or false?

Colour the correct answer.

1. Ping's father caught fish for his family. .... ⃝ **true** ⃝ **false**

2. The cormorants were regular visitors to the boat. .... ⃝ **true** ⃝ **false**

3. Ping was happy living in Hong Kong. .... ⃝ **true** ⃝ **false**

4. Ping cooked the meals for her family. .... ⃝ **true** ⃝ **false**

5. Ping was very courageous. .... ⃝ **true** ⃝ **false**

6. The family slept on the deck. .... ⃝ **true** ⃝ **false**

Reading for understanding

Use full sentences to answer these questions.

1. Why do you think Ping's father used diving birds (cormorants) to catch the fish?

    _____
    _____
    _____

2. Madame Cheng was very mean. What do you think she would do to her victims?

    _____
    _____
    _____

3. Why do you think the sails were made of bamboo?

    _____
    _____
    _____

4. Why do you think Madame Cheng said that Ping reminded her of herself?

    _____
    _____
    _____

Applying your knowledge

1. Many people in Asian countries live and work on boats called junks. What are some of the activities you enjoy doing that Ping wouldn't be able to do? For example: play football, go to the cinema.

   Compile a list of at least 10 activities.

2. Compile a list of advantages of living on a junk.

   _____

   _____

   _____

   _____

3. (a) Ping's father used a cormorant for fishing. What are some other ways of catching fish?

   _____

   _____

   _____

   (b) Describe two different ways of fishing.

   • _____

   _____

   _____

   • _____

   _____

   _____

4. (a) Would you prefer to be a fisherman living on a junk in Hong Kong or one living and working in your country?

   _____

   (b) Explain your answer. _____

   _____

   _____

   _____

1. Dictionary skills

   Use a dictionary to find the meaning of these words.

distant	
harbour	
canopy	
announce	
treacherous	
terrified	
audacity	
miraculous	

2. Base words

   The base word for **surprising** is **surprise**. The base word is the word to which prefixes and suffixes are added.

   What are the base words for these words? Use a dictionary if needed.

   (a) unloved   _____   (b) announced   _____

   (c) heroically   _____   (d) wilderness   _____

   (e) admiration   _____   (f) terrified   _____

   (g) curiosity   _____   (h) impatiently   _____

   (i) reshaped   _____   (j) miraculous   _____

3. Synonyms

   Use a thesaurus to find a synonym (same or similar meaning) for these words.

   (a) brave | | (b) appeared | |

   (c) horizon | | (d) chief | |

   (e) treasure | | (f) following | |

   (g) terrified | | (h) raised | |

4. Definitions

    Sometimes, a single word can be used to replace a phrase; for example, free time – leisure.
    Choose a word from the box below to replace the following phrases.

canopy	meanness	collapsed
distant	horizon	relief
audacity	toothless	celebrate

    (a) the apparent line that divides the earth and sky

    (b) having no teeth

    (c) fell down or caved in suddenly

    (d) far away or apart

    (e) a feeling of cheerfulness that follows the removal of
         pain or distress

    (f) an ornamental awning

    (g) not willing to give or use much of something

    (h) boldness or recklessness

    (i) to hold festivities to mark an event

5. Find these words from *Daring escape* to complete the wordsearch. The words may be
    horizontal, vertical or diagonal.

harbour	bamboo
chief	pirate
terrified	angry
canopy	collapsed
audacity	escape
horizon	morning
relief	sail
miraculous	father
daring	

p	i	r	a	t	e	a	n	g	r	y	t
h	c	h	i	e	f	t	u	s	h	a	b
a	f	m	i	r	a	c	u	l	o	u	s
r	f	a	m	r	l	o	b	g	r	d	t
b	a	d	i	i	c	l	a	t	i	a	m
o	t	b	a	f	t	l	m	u	z	c	o
u	h	s	c	i	d	a	b	f	o	i	r
r	e	l	i	e	f	p	o	s	n	t	n
t	r	w	s	d	u	s	o	g	w	y	i
e	e	s	c	a	p	e	v	w	o	x	n
c	a	n	o	p	y	d	a	r	i	n	g

1. Plurals

    Plural – means more than one. Look at these plurals from the story. Write the singular form next to each one.

    (a) cormorants

    (b) birds

    (c) poles

    (d) friends

    (e) meals

    (f) quarters

    (g) parents

    (h) waters

    (i) pirates

    (j) treasures

    (k) How have these plurals been formed? _____

    _____

2. 'Families' and 'stories' are also plurals from the story.

    Write the singular form of each.

    (a) families

    (b) stories

    Spelling rule

    When words end in **y** the rule is – **y** changes to **i**, then **es** is added.

    (c) List eight words whose plurals are formed this way. Write the plural form next to them.

singular	plural
family	families
story	stories

In the story there are two irregular plurals – fish and fishermen.

For example: one fish   ten fish   one fisherman   ten fishermen

3. Complete the irregular plurals for these words.

(a) woman _____   (b) policeman _____

(c) sheep _____   (d) tooth _____

(e) goose _____   (f) foot _____

(g) child _____   (h) deer _____

(i) salmon _____   (j) cactus _____

Syllables

A syllable is a part of a word containing one vowel sound. Understanding syllables is very helpful in spelling.

For example: foot   football   footballer

one syllable   two syllables   three syllables

4. How many syllables are in each word? Remember, the number of syllables is the same as the number of vowel sounds.

(a) daughter ☐

(b) father ☐

(c) cormorant ☐

(d) horizon ☐

(e) canopy ☐

(f) care ☐

(g) fisherman ☐

(h) could ☐

5. Syllabify these words. Refer to separating syllables on page 8 before starting this exercise. The first one is done for you.

(a) af/ter/noon

(b) a p p e a r e d

(c) t o o t h l e s s

(d) r e t o r t e d

(e) m o r n i n g

(f) c a u g h t

(g) s e c o n d

(h) p a t r o l l i n g

(i) o n l y

(j) d a i l y

(k) m i r a c u l o u s

Adjectives

1. Write five positive and five negative adjectives to describe:

(a) pirates

(b) boats

Positives	Negatives

Positives	Negatives

Comparing adjectives

When using adjectives to compare **one** thing with another, we usually add **er**.

For example: My mother is **old**.   Your mother is **older**.

To compare **more than two things**, we usually add **est**.

For example: She is the **wisest** teacher in this school.

Sometimes before adding **er** or **est**, the last letter is doubled.

For example: His hat is **bigger** than mine.

Their cat is the **fattest** in the street.

2. Try these:

(a) Bob is small. His sister is _____. The baby is the _____.

(b) The tree is big. That one is _____. The giant one is the _____.

(c) I am neat. My sister is _____. My mother is the _____.

(d) Tom is thin. Peter is _____. I am the _____.

Comparatives and superlatives

Comparatives compare **two** people or things. Superlatives compare **more than two** people or things.

For example: pretty   prettier   prettiest

Before adding **er** or **est** to words ending in **y**, we need to change the **y** to **i**.

For example: busy   busier   busiest

3.   Complete this table. Don't forget the spelling rules!

Word	Comparative	Superlative
fussy		
	happier	
		noisiest
funny		
	sandier	
		quietest
silly		
	fussier	
		wealthiest
sunny		

4.   Write the correct form of adjective in each sentence.

(a)   He is the (tall) _____ boy in the team.

(b)   My sister is the (pretty) _____ .

(c)   This dog is (clever) _____ than yours.

(d)   My appointment is (early) _____ than Bill's.

(e)   Mum's apple pies are (tasty) _____ than this one.

(f)   Jack is the (fast) _____ runner in our team.

(g)   The water in the river is (cold) _____ than the ocean.

(h)   This afternoon is (cloudy) _____ than this morning.

(i)   My surfboard is (heavy) _____ than yours.

(j)   This is the (rough) _____ section of the road.

Sometimes, instead of adding **er** or **est**, other words are used.

For example: fabulous   more fabulous   most fabulous

5. Complete this table showing comparatives and superlatives.

	Adjective	Comparative	Superlative
(a)	cheerful		
(b)	famous		
(c)	careless		
(d)	foolish		
(e)	active		
(f)	delicious		
(g)	poisonous		
(h)	comfortable		
(i)	interesting		

6. Some adjectives have irregular comparative and superlative forms.

Learn these and complete the sentences.

Adjective	Comparative	Superlative
little	less	least
good	better	best
bad	worse	worst
many/much	more	most
far	farther/further	farthest/furthest

(a) Berlin had its _____ snowstorm in years.

(b) Berlin had _____ snow than Moscow.

(c) My new car is really good and much _____ than yours.

(d) My house is the _____ from school.

(e) My air ticket was cheap and cost _____ than Bill's.

Punctuation

Commas

Commas are used in sentences when a pause is needed. Read the following sentences carefully to help you to understand more about commas and how they are used to:

- separate items in a list

    My favourite pastimes are watching television, playing computer games, chess and reading.

- separate clauses (A group of words with a verb and subject)

    I climbed into the boat, picked up my rod and reel, baited the hook and threw it into the water.

- indicate a pause after 'yes' or 'no'

    Yes, I would like to go fishing with you.

- separate the person spoken to

    Lee, would you please show me how to do it?

- separate words giving more information

    Waterskiing, a popular sport, is great exercise.

- indicate a pause after direct speech

    'We will be home by five o'clock', Dad promised.

7. Add commas where needed in these sentences.

   (a) We needed to buy butter milk sultanas flour eggs sugar and cream to make the cake.

   (b) The children walked to the park climbed on the monkey bars tried out the swings then played on the grass.

   (c) No I won't be able to attend the party.

   (d) Thomas you haven't completed your work.

   (e) The tall man a well-known footballer was signing autographs in the shopping centre.

   (f) 'Hurry up and get ready' said Mum impatiently.

   (g) Yes I did my homework.

   (h) Zac where did you leave your glasses?

   (i) The band Tomorrow's Guys will be playing here tomorrow.

   (j) 'Please let me go to the beach' Sarah begged.

Direct speech

The exact words that people say or think are referred to as direct speech and must be punctuated correctly.

These words need to be enclosed within speech or quotation marks.

For example: 'I want an ice-cream', demanded Chloe.

NOTE: Single or double quotation marks are accepted but must be used consistently.

Quotation marks are easy if you think of them as 'holding' the actual words spoken.

Punctuating quotations

Punctuating quotations is more of a challenge.

Remember:

- Start every quotation with a capital letter unless it is not a new sentence.

- Every new speaker needs to start on a new line.

- There is often a punctuation mark after the quotation (comma, question mark, exclamation mark or a full stop).

Study the punctuation used in this dialogue.

> 'I think our team will win on Saturday', Tom boasted as he rode home from school.
>
> 'They haven't got a hope of winning', replied Ben.
>
> 'Why not?' asked Tom.
>
> 'They're useless', said Ben, and he rode off.
>
> 'Wait!' yelled Tom as he pedalled after him.
>
> 'I think they can win,' Tom panted, 'but it will be a close game'.

8. Rewrite the dialogue below with correct punctuation.

    First (a) Underline the direct speech.

    (b) Check that you have a punctuation mark at the end of each direct speech.

    (c) Check capital letters at the beginning of each quote.

    (d) Check each new speaker is on a new line.

    Why can't we go to the beach demanded Monique. I told you before replied Dad it is just too windy. We'd be blown away. It's not fair Monique yelled as she stomped away.

Characters

Good writers make characters seem real so that readers know about their appearance, their personality and their likely actions. Readers also need to add their own ideas to further 'see' and 'understand' these characters. For example:

Pirate Pete

Pirate Pete was a mean, miserable man. People knew he was approaching because of the unpleasant musty smell of his stained, ragged clothes and the battered pipe permanently attached to his dry, cracked lips. His injured leg made a distinctive dragging noise and he coughed continuously.

He wore a faded scarf around his weatherbeaten neck in a futile attempt to conceal his mutilated left ear. The gnarled, heavy stick he carried, and which he was only too willing to use on anyone unfortunate and stupid enough to cross his path, ensured that he was feared and avoided by the locals.

1. Use the information given about Pirate Pete and your imagination to complete this character profile.

Appearance

- facial features
  - eyes _____
    _____
  - mouth _____
    _____
  - nose _____
    _____
  - expression _____
    _____

- size and shape _____
  _____

- movements _____
  _____

- clothing _____
  _____

- personality _____
  _____

- other characteristics _____
  _____

2. Write a passage to describe Madame Cheng using the information given in the narrative and your imagination.

_____

_____

_____

_____

_____

_____

_____

_____

_____

_____

_____

_____

_____

_____

_____

Writing a narrative

Choose a topic from the box below and write a narrative. Use the plan on the next page to guide your ideas. When you are ready, write the story in full on a separate sheet of paper.

> *Flirting with danger*
>
> *A narrow escape*
>
> *Lost treasure*
>
> *Terror at sea*
>
> *Pirate island*
>
> *Island cruise*

Use this framework to help you plan your story.

TITLE	
ORIENTATION Characters – (appearance, personality, likely actions)	
Setting/Location	
Time	
INITIATING EVENT What event starts the action?	
How did this involve the characters?	
COMPLICATION What problems do the characters have?	
What caused the problems?	
RESOLUTION How are the problems solved?	
CONCLUSION What happened in the end?	

When you have completed your story, proofread and edit it using the following questions as a guide.

Checklist

Title: _____

1. Title

(a)   Does the title indicate what the story is about?............................. ◯ **yes** ◯ **no**

(b)   Does it get the attention of the reader? .... ◯ **yes** ◯ **no**

2. Orientation

(a)   Does the beginning draw the reader into the characters' world?.... ◯ **yes** ◯ **no**

(b)   Are the characters believable? .... ◯ **yes** ◯ **no**

(c)   Do their actions fit their personalities?... ◯ **yes** ◯ **no**

(d)   Is the setting realistic? .... ◯ **yes** ◯ **no**

3. Initiating event

Is the problem known at the beginning of the story?............................. ◯ **yes** ◯ **no**

4. Complication

Is the problem believable?... ◯ **yes** ◯ **no**

5. Resolution

(a)   Does the resolution fit the complication?...................................... ◯ **yes** ◯ **no**

(b)   Have the problems been solved? .... ◯ **yes** ◯ **no**

6. Conclusion

Is the ending satisfying to the reader? .... ◯ **yes** ◯ **no**

7. Punctuation and spelling

Have you checked the following?

(a)   Spelling – use a dictionary or ask someone .... ◯ **yes** ◯ **no**

(b)   Punctuation – including capital letters, full stops,
question marks, commas and direct speech.................................. ◯ **yes** ◯ **no**

(c)   Paragraphs for new ideas.. ◯ **yes** ◯ **no**

8. Vocabulary

(a)   Have you used some interesting adjectives? .... ◯ **yes** ◯ **no**

(b)   Have you used any compound words? .... ◯ **yes** ◯ **no**

(c)   Have you used more interesting verbs instead of 'said'?............... ◯ **yes** ◯ **no**

1. Choose a title from the box, then plan and write a **narrative**.

   > *The menacing pirate*
   >
   > *My island home*
   >
   > *Treasure Island*
   >
   > *Caught in a storm*
   >
   > *Shipwrecked*
   >
   > *Chinese adventure*

2. A narrative has five parts.

   (a) The _____ indicates what the story is about.

   (b) The _____ describes who, what, where and when.

   (c) The _____ describes the problem facing the main character(s).

   (d) The _____ describes how the problem is solved.

   (e) The _____ tells what happens at the end.

3. Base words

   Find the base words for the following.

   (a) adventurous _____

   (b) following _____

   (c) unhappy _____

   (d) celebration _____

4. Synonyms

   Find a synonym for these words.

   (a) treasure _____

   (b) terrified _____

   (c) laugh _____

   (d) appeared _____

5. Replace the following phrases with a single word from the box.

junk	bamboo
cormorant	reward

   (a) a diving sea bird with lustrous black plumage

   (b) a flat-bottomed sailing vessel

   (c) a return or recompense for service or merit

   (d) a mainly tropical, giant, woody grass

6. Write the plurals of the following words, using the spelling rules you have learnt.

   (a) puppy _____

   (b) woman _____

   (c) potato _____

   (d) dingo _____

   (e) octopus _____

   (f) island _____

   (g) canopy _____

   (h) daisy _____

   (i) avocado _____

   (j) afternoon _____

7. Syllabify these words.

    (a) t r e a s u r e   (b) w a t c h   (c) h a r b o u r   (d) p i r a t e

8. Comparing adjectives

    Complete this table. Don't forget the spelling rules or that some adjectives are irregular.

Word	Comparative	Superlative
white		
	scarier	
	better	
		cleverest
		most
noisy		
	more precious	
expensive		

9. Punctuation

    Add commas where needed in the following sentences.

    > As I was walking to school I saw my friend Anna the captain of the netball team. She was holding her satchel containing her books pencil case lunch gym shoes and a school blazer.
    >
    > 'Are you coming to practice tonight?' Anna enquired.
    >
    > 'Yes I will be there' I answered.

10. Direct speech

    Rewrite this dialogue with the correct punctuation.

    > Have you cleaned up your room yet called Mum. No I have been helping Dad in the garden Jane answered.
    >
    > Where is he now asked Mum. He's just cleaning up then he'll be in for lunch Jane replied.

    _____

    _____

    _____

    _____

    _____

Magnifying lenses

Reports give facts clearly without unnecessary information or opinions.

Read the **report**.

Magnifying lenses

Introduction

Although the Egyptians and Phoenicians made glass over 3000 years ago, it was not until some time before the year 1200 that an unknown inventor in China or Europe made a curved lens.

At that time, scientists did not understand about light, but they noticed that the curved lens changed the way things looked.

The first lenses

The word 'lens' came from the Latin word for lentil, because the first lenses looked similar in shape to lentil seeds.

In 1280 an Italian inventor, probably a man named Salvino degli Armati, fitted two lenses side by side to make eyeglasses. But people with poor eyesight just had to manage as best they could for many years until eyeglasses were readily available.

Early spectacles

The first glasses, known as 'discs for the eyes', were not made of glass. They were made from crystals of a mineral called 'beryl', which although not as clear as glass, was tough and easier to shape and polish.

The frames were made of wood or animal bone.

Eyeglasses were first sold to the public in Italy in 1451. Early spectacles were worn wedged on the nose.

Cheap glasses with metal frames went on sale to the public in the 1800s.

New improved lenses

It took scientists another 200 years to put lenses together in line, instead of side by side, to make microscopes and telescopes. In 1590 Zacharias Jansen made the first microscope and the first telescope was invented in 1608.

Scientific knowledge, especially in the field of medicine, was facilitated by the development of microscopes.

Medical scientists learnt more about the human body, enabling them to effectively treat many illnesses.

Telescopes advanced human understanding of the universe and led to the development of space programmes which have contributed to technology in many ways, particularly in the area of communication.

Today, most spectacle lenses and frames are made of tough plastic, as are contact lenses, which were first developed in 1887.

Class activity

1. Brainstorm the advantages and disadvantages of wearing glasses.

2. Discuss the reasons why people may need to wear glasses.

3. Compile a list of things we can do to protect our eyes.

Partner activity

1. Talk with your partner about some famous people you know who wear glasses. Compile a list.

2. Discuss with your partner any friends or relatives who wear glasses or contact lenses.

3. Talk about how people who wear glasses may feel about them and why they may choose to wear contact lenses instead.

Structure of a report

This report has:	**A title:**	Identifies the subject of the report.
	Classification:	What is it? Provides information about the focus of the report.
	Description:	When they were invented?
		Who invented them?
		How they developed?
		Where they are used?
	Conclusion:	A summary or comment.

Read the report *Magnifying lenses* and answer the questions.

TITLE

(a) What is the title of the report?

_____

(b) Write an appropriate alternative title.

_____

CLASSIFICATION

What is a magnifying lens?

_____

DESCRIPTION

(a) Where did the word 'lens' originate?

_____

(b) What was one disadvantage of using beryl?

_____

(c) When and where were eyeglasses first sold to the public?

_____

(d) What are two other uses for magnifying lenses?

_____

_____

CONCLUSION

What are most lenses and frames made of today?

_____

WORKING WITH THE TEXT   Reading

Reading for information
True or false? Colour the correct answer.

1. Glass has been produced for over 3000 years.   ○ **true** ○ **false**

2. The first glasses, known as 'discs for the eyes', were made of glass.   ○ **true** ○ **false**

3. Eyeglasses were first sold to the public in Italy in 1651.   ○ **true** ○ **false**

4. Cheap glasses with metal frames went on sale to the public in the 1800s.   ○ **true** ○ **false**

5. The first microscope was invented in 1590 by Zacharias Jansen.   ○ **true** ○ **false**

Reading for understanding

1. Give some reasons why it took so long for glasses to become readily available.

_____

_____

_____

2. Why was the invention of the microscope so important?

_____

_____

_____

3. Why was the telescope useful to our understanding of the universe?

_____

_____

_____

4. How has plastic changed the wearing of glasses?

_____

_____

_____

Applying your knowledge

'Magnification' makes objects appear larger. The amount of magnification can vary. Use the grid system to magnify the drawing of a butterfly x 3 and x 8.

Magnified x 3

Magnified x 8

Alliteration

'Alliteration' is the repeated use of the same sound or letter at the beginning of two or more words close together. It can be used to great effect in advertisements, newspapers, proverbs, poetry and other forms of writing.

For example: The **s**limy, **s**lippery **s**nake **s**lid into the **s**hadowy **s**traw.

1. Create your own alliteration using adjectives (descriptive words) for these nouns.

(a) _____ _____ basketballers

(b) _____ _____ swimmers

(c) _____ _____ caterpillars

(d) _____ _____ worms

(e) _____ _____ flowers

(f) _____ _____ trees

(g) _____ _____ boys

(h) _____ _____ girls

(i) _____ _____ ships

(j) _____ _____ boats

Adverbs

Adverbs (words to modify or add to the meaning of verbs) can also be used for alliteration.

For example: swimming swiftly

singing sweetly

2. Add adverbs to these verbs to create alliteration.

(a) ran _____

(b) sipped _____

(c) walking _____

(d) jumping _____

(e) laughed _____

(f) hopping _____

(g) sleeping _____

(h) climbing _____

(i) stared _____

(j) drove _____

Word pairs

3. Words are often paired or associated with each other.

    For example: cup and saucer.

    Complete the following word pairs.

(a) salt and

(b) knife and

(c) table and

(d) bread and

(e) art and

(f) shoes and

(g) pins and

(h) needle and

(i) sons and

(j) bits and

(k) fish and

(l) shirt and

Words to replace phrases

4. Often, we can use a single word to replace a phrase.

    For example: free time – leisure.

    Choose one of the words in the box to replace each phrase.

(a) to do over again   _____

(b) to last for a short time   _____

(c) calm and peaceful   _____

(d) a meat eater   _____

(e) no longer in existence   _____

(f) talk given in a church   _____

(g) let go   _____

(h) not very good quality   _____

(i) not very clear   _____

(j) a small town   _____

(k) someone who speaks   _____

(l) to say you will not accept   _____

(m) to find the place of   _____

(n) to put your name down   _____

locate	obscure
repeat	village
speaker	released
carnivore	enrol
sermon	temporary
extinct	refuse
inferior	tranquil

Alphabet addition

5. Use the initial letter plus the given clue to form the new word. The first one has been done for you.

(a) A + a labyrinth = surprise or astound

> A + maze = amaze

(b) B + opposite to left = shiny or intelligent (6)

(c) C + warmth = to play unfairly (5)

(d) D + fire residue = a mark used to join words (4)

(e) E + to say = a piece of landed property (6)

(f) F + anger = something hot (4)

(g) G + male sheep = unit of weight (4)

(h) H + a joining word = a body part (4)

(i) I + a degree of speed = angry (5)

(j) J + a female relative = a short journey (5)

(k) K + an indication of a maiden name = a body part (4)

(l) L + frozen water = plural of louse (4)

(m) M + a word meaning to consume = animal flesh (4)

(n)   N + an imperial land measure = mother-of-pearl (5)

(o)   O + a writing implement = the opposite of closed (4)

(p)   P + something used to hear = a fruit (4)

(q)   Q(u) + opposite of difficult = nauseous (6)

(r)   R + a top card or tennis shot = a running competition (4)

(s)   S + to listen = to cut a sheep's fleece (5)

(t)   T + having sufficient power or strength = a piece of furniture (5)

(u)   U + profoundly wise person = the act of using or employing (5)

(v)   V + a cry of pain = to give one's assurance (5)

(w) W + the back of the foot = a circular frame which turns on an axis (5)

(x)   X + a sunbeam = pictures of inside the body (4)

(y)   Y + a listening organ = a period of 52 weeks (4)

(z)   Z + the first number = an area or district (4)

Plurals

Revision

There are a number of spelling rules for changing singular nouns (one) to plural (more than one).

- Usually we just add **s**.

  For example: one book   two book**s**

- We need to add **es** to nouns ending with:

  ch   **sh**   **o**   **s**   **x**   and   **z**

  because it usually makes them easier to say.

  For example: lunch**es**, dish**es**, potato**es**, atlas**es**, box**es**, waltz**es**

- Words ending with **f** or **fe** change to **ves**.

  For example: calf   calves

                  life   lives

To revise these rules and the exceptions, refer back to pages 85.

1. Change these words from singular to plural.

    (a) beach   _____   (b) fox   _____

    (c) footballer _____   (d) yourself   _____

    (e) shelf   _____   (f) potato   _____

    (g) watch   _____   (h) stadium   _____

    (i) outdoor   _____   (j) half   _____

Rule

Words ending in **y** after a consonant change the **y** to **i** before adding **es**.

For example: story   stories

                baby   babies

2. Write the plurals of these words.

    (a) activity   (b) library

    (c) puppy   (d) hobby

    (e) responsibility   (f) key

    (g) donkey   (h) display

Changed vowels

The vowels are changed in some words to form plurals.

For example: man   men

3.   Write the plurals of these words.

(a) tooth

(b) goose

(c) foot

(d) gentleman

(e) woman

(f) crisis

No change

Some nouns have the same singular and plural forms.

For example: The injured **sheep** didn't stay with all the other **sheep** in the paddock.

The fisherman removed the **cod** he'd just caught from the hook and put it in the tub with the five **cod** he'd caught earlier.

4.   Write two sentences using each noun.

One should be as a singular noun and the other a plural noun. The first one has been done.

innings

He played one very good **innings**.

Ken scored a century in his two **innings**.

sheep

reindeer

cod

No singular

Some nouns have no singular form. Some things that come in pairs are sometimes already plurals.

For example: jean**s**   tweezer**s**

5.   Complete these sentences.

(a) Older people often need g_____ to read.

(b) P_____ should be comfortable to wear to bed.

(c) The birdwatcher forgot to take his b_____ with him.

(d) Use those t_____ to lift the hot potatoes out of the oven.

(e) His t_____ were made of fine merino wool and fitted him well.

Confusing words

Some words are confused because they sound similar but have different meanings.

For example: accept and except

Some words are confused because the noun (naming word) and verb (doing word) sound similar.

For example: effect and affect
                advice and advise

> **Accept** is 'to agree to take something or somebody'.
>
> **Except** means that 'something is not included'.

> **Effect** is a noun, so you can say 'the effect'.
>
> **Affect** is a verb, so it is something that makes a difference.

6.   Choose the right word to complete these sentences.

(a) Everyone _____ Joshua was invited to the party.

(b) Chloe did not _____ her invitation.

(c) Olivia hoped that Sophie would _____ and attend the party.

(d) The food was delicious _____ for the cold sausage rolls.

7.   Use the correct word to complete these sentences.

(a) The cyclone had a devastating _____ on the town.

(b) How did it _____ you?

(c) Communication to the whole area was _____ed.

(d) One _____ of the storm was that roads had to be closed.

> **Advice** (noun) Listen to my advice.
>
> **Advise** (verb) I advise you to listen.

8. Write a sentence using each word correctly.

(a) advice _____

_____

(b) advise _____

_____

Some words are confused because, although they sound the same, the noun and verb are spelt differently. These are called homophones.

For example: practice and practise

licence and license

> **Practice** (noun) Do some practice tonight.
>
> **Practise** (verb) Practise the recorder later.

9. Choose the correct word to complete these sentences.

(a) I don't want to _____ now.

(b) You must do some _____.

(c) I think _____ is a waste of time.

(d) Riley does some _____ every day.

> **Licence** (noun) Where is my driver's licence?
>
> **License** (verb) I must license my motorbike.

10. Choose the correct word to complete these sentences.

(a) I passed my driver's _____ yesterday.

(b) You need a _____ to catch crayfish.

(c) The traffic office will not _____ my car until I fix the tyres.

Prepositions

Prepositions connect one thing with another showing how they are related.

For example: **After** taking his patient's temperature **with** a thermometer, the doctor looked **at** it and put it **in** his pocket.

1. Complete each sentence using a preposition from the box.

| after | with | in | while | at | outside |

(a) Emma had to visit the dentist ☐ school.

(b) She went ☐ her mother.

(c) Sitting waiting ☐ the surgery was very boring.

(d) At last the dentist told her to sit ☐ the chair.

(e) ☐ she had her mouth open, the dentist asked lots of questions.

(f) Her mother dropped her back ☐ school before lunch.

Prepositions are followed by a **noun**, **noun phrase** or **pronoun**.

For example: The children are hiding <u>behind</u> **the shed** – noun.

Put your books <u>on</u> **the round table** – noun phrase.

Give the books <u>to</u> **him** – pronoun.

2. All the highlighted words can be prepositions but only when followed by a noun, noun phrase or pronoun. Colour **yes** or **no** to indicate if they are prepositions in these sentences.

(a) The helicopter flew **above** the cliffs. ◯ yes ◯ no

(b) I saw a whale **at** the beach. ◯ yes ◯ no

(c) The teacher threw his hat **down**. ◯ yes ◯ no

(d) Pick that ball **up**. ◯ yes ◯ no

(e) He leans **against** the fence. ◯ yes ◯ no

(f) Isabella gave her chocolates **to** me. ◯ yes ◯ no

(g) Our house is **opposite** the park. ◯ yes ◯ no

(h) Our class went camping **for** the weekend. ◯ yes ◯ no

(i) He watched the aircraft **above**. ◯ yes ◯ no

(j) When we went to the beach, we left our dog **behind**. ◯ yes ◯ no

Note:

The words that are not prepositions in Question 2 are **adverbs** because they describe how, when or where something happened.

For example: He ran **behind**.   Behind is an **adverb** telling where he ran.

Confused prepositions

among and **between**

Things are shared **between** two people and **among** three or more people.

We walk **between** two trees and we walk **among** many trees.

3. Write **among** or **between** in each sentence.

    (a) The staff distributed the prizes [   ] the students.

    (b) My sister and I ate the cake [   ] us.

    (c) The four goals scored in the game were shared [   ] the three forwards.

    (d) The two thieves divided the money [   ] them.

    (e) We swam [   ] many shoals of fish.

Confused verbs

bought and **brought**

Because **bought** and **brought** look and sound alike they can be confusing.

Remember: **br**ought is the past tense of **br**ing.   Think **br**

bought is the past tense of **b**uy.   Think **b**

4. Write **bought** or **brought** in each sentence.

    (a) The teacher _____ his stamp collection to school and showed us the

    new stamp he _____ in America.

    (b) The school _____ some magnifying lenses so the pupils could

    examine the insects they _____ to school.

    (c) I _____ a skateboard for my birthday and I've _____
    it to show you.

seen and **saw**

Seen and **saw** are both PAST TENSE verbs. **Saw** is used alone. **Seen** is used with a 'helper' or helpers.

For example: I **saw** a gigantic shark yesterday.

               I **have seen** a gigantic shark.

               A gigantic shark **was seen** yesterday.

               A gigantic shark may have **been seen**.

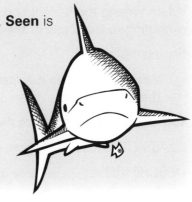

5.   Write **seen** or **saw** to complete these sentences.

(a) I _____ you at the beach.

(b) The intruder was _____ creeping behind the shed.

(c) The airline pilot _____ the runway lights.

(d) I've _____ this film before.

(e) The horse _____ its owner and galloped towards her.

(f) The thief was _____ climbing in the window.

(g) He hasn't been _____ since yesterday.

(h) We _____ the light twinkling in the distance.

did and **done**

Did and **done** are both PAST TENSE verbs. **Did** is used alone. **Done** needs a 'helper' or 'helpers'.

For example: I **did** my homework last night.

               My homework **was done** last night.

               My sister **should have done** her homework too.

6.   Write **did** or **done** to complete these sentences.

(a) Sean _____ the dishes.

(b) Put your hand up when you've _____ the worksheet.

(c) We _____ it.

(d) He's _____ all the gardening.

(e) I think that you should have _____ your homework.

(f) Where _____ you put it?

(g) My father has _____ a great job of fixing my bike.

(h) The baking was _____ very quickly.

Descriptions

When writing the description part of a report, the information or facts provided change according to the focus of the report as stated in the classification.

For example:

When writing about a machine, the focus may be on the uses of the machine rather than its appearance.

You might include some of the following facts.

CLASSIFICATION: Name of the machine

DESCRIPTION: Why it is used?

When it is used?

How it is used?

1. Write a description suitable for a report about a machine you use or are familiar with; for example: a microwave, CD player. Remember to write FACTS not OPINIONS and to focus on **why**, **when** and **how** it is used. Use clear and concise language and technical terms.

CLASSIFICATION:

_____

DESCRIPTION:

_____

_____

_____

_____

_____

_____

_____

_____

_____

_____

_____

Mystery machine

2. (a) Write a description of a machine using clear, concise and some technical language. Remember to focus on **why**, **when** and **how** it is used.

CLASSIFICATION: Mystery Machine

DESCRIPTION:

_____

_____

_____

_____

_____

_____

_____

_____

_____

_____

_____

(b) Ask a partner to identify your mystery machine and to draw it on a separate sheet of paper.

(c) Did your partner solve the 'mystery'?

_____

Choose a topic for a report from the box below and use the plan to prepare it.

Remember to use **facts** not **opinions** and technical terms where appropriate.

You may need to research information for your topic.

television	*walkman*	*microscope*	*telescope*
binoculars	*prisms*	*clocks*	

TITLE: _____

CLASSIFICATION: (type) _____

_____

DESCRIPTION:

Appearance: _____   Inventor: _____

_____   _____

_____   _____

_____   _____

Function: _____   Place and time of invention: _____

_____   _____

_____   _____

_____   _____

Any other relevant facts _____

_____

_____

_____

_____

_____

Conclusion _____

_____

_____

After you have written your report in full on a separate sheet of paper, use the checklist below to edit and proofread your work.

You will self-edit for:

Spelling   Punctuation

Grammar   Sentence structure

You will use a peer editor to check for:

Sense

That you have used facts

Checklist

Title of report: _____

1. Does your report include:

   (a) the appearance? ....○ **yes** ○ **no**

   (b) the function? ....○ **yes** ○ **no**

   (c) inventor? ....○ **yes** ○ **no**

   (d) place and time of invention? ....○ **yes** ○ **no**

   (e) any other relevant facts? ....○ **yes** ○ **no**

2. Have you written facts, not opinions? ....○ **yes** ○ **no**

3. Do you have a concluding statement? ....○ **yes** ○ **no**

4. Have you corrected any spelling errors? ....○ **yes** ○ **no**

5. Have you used capital letters and full stops correctly? ...○ **yes** ○ **no**

6. Did your peer editor:

   (a) understand your report? ....○ **yes** ○ **no**

   (b) believe your facts are true? ....○ **yes** ○ **no**

1. Choose a topic from the box below and write a report. Use a report plan to help you to organise your ideas before writing your report in full on a separate sheet of paper.

cameras	*microwaves*	*alarm clocks*
biros	*DVD players*	*hair dryers*

2. Reports should provide facts not _____ and should not have

    unnecessary _____.

3. Create your own alliteration using adjectives for these nouns.

    (a) [_____] , [_____] dogs

    (b) [_____] , [_____] tigers

    (c) [_____] , [_____] river

4. Write the plural of these words.

    (a) half _____   (b) box _____

    (c) church _____   (d) wish _____

    (e) tomato _____   (f) athlete _____

    (g) duty _____   (h) monkey _____

    (i) woman _____   (j) mouse _____

    (k) deer _____   (l) camera _____

5. Circle the correct word in the brackets.

    (a) Everyone (accept/except) me is allowed to go.

    (b) Please (accept/except) my apology for being late.

    (c) In science we studied the (effect/affect) of pollution.

    (d) The rain had a positive (affect/effect) on the crops.

    (e) Please (advice/advise) me when the parcel arrives.

    (f) Grandma gave the children lots of (advice/advise).

    (g) Our team (practise/practice) was cancelled.

    (h) Please (practise/practice) multiplication of fractions.

    (i) My brother passed his driver's (license/licence) test.

6. Underline the prepositions in each sentence.

> Last Thursday we went on the bus to Kangaroo Island. We stayed until Sunday in small cottages near the beach. One group was taken fishing in a beautiful boat; one abseiled down a cliff and another snorkelled under the jetty.

7. Are the highlighted words prepositions? Circle **yes** or **no**.

(a) The seagull flew **over** the wharf.　　　　　　　○ **yes** ○ **no**

(b) One of the buttons **on** my jacket is loose.　　　○ **yes** ○ **no**

(c) Can you see the beautiful rainbow **above**?　　　○ **yes** ○ **no**

(d) We have played this game **before**.　　　　　　○ **yes** ○ **no**

(e) He ran to the edge of the pool and jumped **in**.　○ **yes** ○ **no**

(f) I was scared when the cockroach crawled **on** me.　○ **yes** ○ **no**

(g) The aircraft flew **around**.　　　　　　　　　　○ **yes** ○ **no**

(h) Put your shoes **under** the bed.　　　　　　　　○ **yes** ○ **no**

8. Circle the correct word in the brackets.

> (a) Share these books (among/between) the class members.

> (b) Dad (bought/brought) home the new car he (bought/brought) on Tuesday.

> (c) The patient (saw/seen) the doctor.

> (d) I've (did/done) all my shopping.

> (e) Haven't we (saw/seen) this film before?

> (f) The ball went (among/between) the goal posts.

> (g) The team have (did/done) their very best to reach the grand final.

> (h) Please (accept/except) my apologies.

> (i) You need to do more (practice/practise).

> (j) If I need your (advise/advice) I'll ask for it.